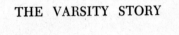

THE VARSITY STORY

THE
VARSITY STORY

BY

MORLEY CALLAGHAN

ILLUSTRATED BY
ERIC ALDWINCKLE, O.S.A.

TORONTO

THE MACMILLAN COMPANY

OF CANADA LIMITED

1948

Printed in Canada

University of Toronto Press

CONTENTS

CHAPTER ONE

RIVING at night up University Avenue in Toronto you come to College Street and Queen's Park and there, directly ahead, blocking the way, are the massive heavy-set brownstone Parliament Buildings. The Avenue splits into two crescents which circle the little park with its old trees. At night-time the headlights of the cars coming around the park make the two crescents look like a spinning lighted pin wheel. The swinging headlights begin to flash on turrets and towers and on the stone faces of buildings that do not seem to belong to the rest of the big sprawling industrial city. Lights gleam for a moment on the Gothic lines and pointed roofs of those buildings to the right. Ahead at the turn a tower rises against the night sky. At the corner there is the gleaming reflection of long abbey-like windows. And veering round the crescent the ribbons of light criss-cross and play on a little cluster of turrets and towers and minarets and chimneys and what looks like a Norman keep. Soon the lights and the shadows begin to

1

play tricks with the imagination. Across a little valley is what seems to be a village green, with the dome of the town hall outlined against the sky on the other side of the green. It looks like an old town. And it is too. It is a university town there in the heart of a big industrial city.

Toronto citizens giving an address sometimes will say, "It is in the University neighbourhood." That neighbourhood takes in all those side streets: Breadalbane, St. Mary, Charles, Isabella, Huron, Madison, Sussex, where the students from the University in their little rooms nurse the bright dreams they brought to Toronto. But on those same side streets, in those same rooming-houses, and in the little shops are thousands of Toronto people who believe that what goes on in this college town can never touch their own city lives.

The factory worker going along College Street at night is sure the University isn't important to him. He never went there, nor will his son. Yet he may be passing the Banting Institute. "Oh, sure, insulin, that's important," he will say. "My brother's diabetic." And the big Connaught laboratories also there on College Street, where they make insulin and products necessary for the prevention of certain diseases? "The stuff they turn out there? Oh sure," he will say. "I know doctors and engineers are important to me too. But it is those intellectuals. They're no skin off my nose one way or another."

Those intellectuals go down town and are hardly noticed, although some citizens maintain that they can recognize them by their manner or their bearing. They seem to be simply a part of the city life. But sometimes a business man, a merchant or a banker, who did not go to the University, is invited to attend a convocation at which a chancellor is to be installed. At the appointed hour he goes in his shining car to Convocation Hall, mingles with other eminent citizens, and perhaps for the first time gazes upon the assembled schoolmen on the rise to the left of the dais, with a strange wonder: it looks like a picture gallery of another age. The rise begins to fill with men and women in gowns splashed with colour, until it is like a rash of fire. Some of them wear little red berets and some have gowns as blue as the sky, and there are flashes of saffron and crimson and red against the black. It is hard for him to believe that these gaily adorned figures are men he has seen walking on the streets of down-town Toronto.

And when he comes out of the hall, before getting into his car he looks around the campus and asks himself if the place really has an atmosphere of its own, a way of life.

But the street cars rattle along College Street, the carillon bells ring, and the students are on the way to their residences or on their way home. On those paths where they walk, many thousands of young men and women in the past have walked, in the time of their lives when their minds were most alive. There are many converging paths: one goes up from Simcoe Hall past the cloisters of University College; one goes across the park and under the trees; one up by the east wing of Trinity and up past the museum to Bloor Street, is a walk for lovers in the spring at examination time. But watching the students walk on the familiar paths won't tell you much about the University or whether it has anything of its own. Of course it has its own residences, and in the mornings the street cars rattling along College, Bay and Bloor bring students from the rooms in the city to become part of its sequestered life. It has its own government: a Chancellor, a President, a Board of Governors, and a Senate composed of representatives from the various Faculties. These governing bodies assemble in impressive chambers in Simcoe Hall to the west of the front campus. It has its own policeman, too. And there is always someone around the campus who likes to talk about life there.

One day in October, back in nineteen twenty-four, a slender man in a brown jacket and gray trousers was crossing Queen's Park on his way to Hart House. It was a fine day and he was without a hat. He had thick black curling hair and blue eyes, and he walked with a quick confident step. He looked like an affable man with a warm manner. His name was Arthur Tyndall, and he was in a good position to know a lot about the University because he was the Warden of Hart House, that noble stone building at the western edge of the park.

Hart House, the assembling place for all men of the University, is right in the centre of university activity. It has a great hall where thousands of students queue up for meals; it has the Faculty dining-room where the Faculty members eat, and a library, a reading-room, a common-room, a sketch room, a theatre, a billiard room, a music room, squash courts, a big gym and a chapel. It is an athletic and cultural centre. It is the great debating hall. It has everything to give the student a community life outside the classroom.

Arthur Tyndall had those qualities necessary to one who could be expected to administer successfully such a large student union. He knew how to get along with men and had a peculiar genius for recognizing who was important and who wasn't, while being charmingly available to everybody. He was a New Zealander, from Wellington, and had spent three years at Oxford. He was beginning his second year at Hart House. In his first year he had won the approval of everybody and no longer thought of himself as a stranger. He was unmarried but there was a Miss Hallam, the daughter of a banker in Wellington, a fine girl whose picture was on the dresser of his bedroom and with whom he corresponded regularly. She was waiting for him to write and tell her that he thought she would be happy with him in Toronto.

In the one year he had spent at Toronto, Tyndall had acquired a lot of knowledge about the city and the University. Students, members of the staff and even the Toronto natives often have only the haziest recollections of the growth of the neighbourhood. But Tyndall, a stranger and conscientious, believed that a man in his position ought to know the history of the place. He had all the facts and all the surface impressions, which he took a special delight in displaying publicly. If he were having lunch with some Faculty member and then after lunch companionably strolling along in the sunlight on the sidewalk by University College he would take his pipe out of his mouth and, pointing at the old College, say, "Did you ever stop to look at the work of the old stonemasons? In their own way they had fun. Come here, I'll show you." And, chuckling to himself, he would lead the way around to the front of the building, go close to the wall, screen his eyes in the sunlight and point up at the carvings high overhead. And then he would point at the second-storey right-wing windows facing the campus and show how the architect had tried to balance that set of windows—which were hardly used as windows, lighting as they did only stacks of books in the college library—with the more formal set to the left of the main entrance. "Astonishing, isn't it?" he would ask. He knew also which parts of that building had been destroyed by fire in the old days. His information always surprised the natives and he knew it and a pleased little smile would come on his face. He had looked into all the forgotten corners. He could point across the park to the Parliament Buildings and tell you they were on the site of the first King's College. He could point to that little gray stone observatory which stands to the right of the east wing of University College and opposite the entrance to Hart House, and explain, "Interesting little place, isn't it? It was the old Magnetic Observatory. Used to stand down there near College Street on

5

the site of the new Physics building. They moved it up here stone by stone." Or he could walk past the back campus and explain that the new Trinity College, in its architectural style, was supposed to adhere as closely as possible to the style of the old Trinity College which still stood some miles away to the west on Queen Street. A little observation about Trinity would lead, of course, to some recollection of that remarkable character, Bishop Strachan; he would discuss aspects of the Bishop's character with his eyes half closed and a slightly cynical smile. He had all the facts. His facts were an embarrassment to the less well-informed natives. It was impossible to think of him as a stranger. But his superior information was so much a part of his open-handed manner that no one resented it. He certainly seemed to be the right man for the Warden's position in Hart House.

As he crossed Queen's Park, with the sun shining on dead leaves and still green grass, those stone buildings—Hart House, University College and, to the left in the little valley, the library—all seemed to be a part of the warm glowing stillness of late sunlight and mist and brownness of the Ontario autumn. By the curving road of the crescent a caretaker was raking the leaves into a bonfire. The smoke drifted up in a slow spiral. On the back campus were other fires, the smoke hovering over the roofs of that red building, Wycliffe. The smell of burning leaves was in the air.

When you cross the road, ducking the automobiles curving round the crescent, you go down into the little valley which was once a river-bed. The green sloping banks are deepest behind the old stone library which rises from the depth of the valley like an ancient massive fortress. On these valley slopes were engineering students with their surveying instruments and their steel tapes, who were busily surveying this plot of ground which had been surveyed by a thousand students in other years.

As Tyndall made the turn towards Hart House, a tall girl in a loose brown coat, with a round face and black hair, was strolling along the path. Helen Winston was her name; she came from a town near Regina and was in her first year at Victoria. Her head was down, for she was reading *The Varsity,* and she didn't notice that a notebook had slipped from under her arm.

"Wait a minute," Tyndall called. His smile was pleasant. "I think you dropped something." And as he picked up the black notebook he read the words, neatly typed on a little white slip which was pasted on the cover, "Economics, 1st year". "Here you are," he said. "You may need this."

"Why, thanks," she said. "Indeed I may need it." She smiled as if she half recognized him but wasn't sure.

"Your first year, I see," he said genially.

"Yes," she said shyly. "Honour English—the pass economics is an extra subject."

"Really," he said. With another charming smile that was like an admonition he doffed his hat politely. "It's a complicated subject. You'd better hang on to that notebook." And he bowed and went on his way.

But before he had taken ten steps he found himself muttering, "Economics. Why would a bright pretty girl like that be bothering with economics?" and he turned to watch her go up the path, hesitate at the crossing, and then go on across the park, walking slowly, her head bowed as she went on reading *The Varsity.* "Well, I suppose it's all in the air now," and he smiled to himself complacently. Tyndall had taken Classics and Philosophy. In those days of the early twenties the sciences and economics were the intellectual fashion. All the students read H. G. Wells. Some read H. L. Mencken. In America it was the jazz age. Tyndall called it all "the new learning".

On the other side of the road, Professor C——, of the English

Department at U. C., passing hurriedly, waved his arm. "Hello, Tyndall," he called. Pointing to the valley where the young engineers with their surveying equipment were industriously practising their art Tyndall called, "A busy day for the practical man, I see," and he grinned. As a lover of the humanities the English professor grinned appreciatively in return. The two lovers of the humanities were having their jest at the practical men swarming on the hills.

Arthur Tyndall often took a little jibe at some aspect of the university life. But he did it so cheerfully that no one noticed how critical he was. He didn't notice it himself. In the Faculties in those days were some men of dry wit, who made quiet jokes about Toronto. Their humour, to Tyndall, seemed to come out of a wider experience with the cosmopolitan world. Dean Alfred DeLury, the mathematician, who had a dry cynical humour and who loved the Irish poets, was such a man. And the dapper Pelham Edgar, of Victoria, a lover of Henry James, and working now on a critical appreciation of the art of the novel, seemed capable of looking reflectively at the life around him. All of these men, and there were at least a dozen of them, did not appear to be Toronto men. Therefore Tyndall, being one of them, was able to joke with them. He could cheerfully regret the lack of criticism in the country and the University, or the plight of an artist or a man of ideas in the country. But whether it was with one of the professors or one of the students he could take this attitude easily; he could do it with the genial affectionate gesture. No one resented his witty little comments. Canadians had such a deprecatory air about themselves anyway. They expected a visitor from other shores to perceive all their weaknesses. And they accepted the critical rebuke with profound humility. Tyndall seemed to have become truly a Canadian because he so quickly learned to play this game. As for his own gentle jokes, he did not believe he was being cynical.

After waving cheerfully to the professor he started to whistle a popular song, "Three O'clock In The Morning". The late sunlight and the smell of burning leaves gave a little lift to his heart. Suddenly he noticed that he was walking in step with a smooth-faced, dark-haired boy with steady brown eyes. This boy was Harry Rigby, a third-year Arts student at Victoria. "Hello, sir," Harry Rigby said.

"Hello there," Arthur Tyndall said briskly. "Going into Hart House?"

"Why, no, I'm going over to St. George Street, Mr. Tyndall."

"I'm sure I've seen you a lot around Hart House, haven't I?"

"No, I don't think so," the student said doubtfully.

"But you do go to Hart House, don't you?"

"Well, yes," the student said, grinning a little. "I go there sometimes to get a haircut."

"Oh. I see. A cultural urge that's pretty hard to resist."

"Well, it's a good barber shop," said the student, playing along with him.

"I see," said Tyndall, who was irritated by the student's tone. He couldn't get used to this North American kidding. "Hart House, I suppose, was intended to be something more than a barber shop, but sometimes I wonder how many of the men are as concerned about the inside of their heads as they are about the outside."

"Don't you think they are, sir?" the student asked seriously.

"I sometimes wonder," Tyndall said, his tone a little cynical.

"I was half kidding, sir. You see, I'm in residence at Victoria. I wouldn't use Hart House as much as some of the students who aren't in residence. I do go to the barber shop, but I also am very interested in the theatre. You shouldn't judge other fellows by what I said, sir."

"Oh, quite, quite," Tyndall said quickly, and as they stood there near the entrance to Hart House there was a sudden embarrassed silence, and the student was surprised because Tyndall seemed to want to apologize to him. He felt uncomfortable.

But Tyndall, too, had been caught off guard. This one student, steady-eyed, yet embarrassed now, realized that he, Tyndall, really had a low opinion of the University. Tyndall had never admitted it to anybody. He had never admitted it to himself. His face reddened. He wanted to get away from the surprised expression in the student's eyes. "Well, cheerio," he said lightly and hurried into Hart House.

The little incident troubled Tyndall the rest of the afternoon. Even when he was having a conference with the Comptroller of Hart House he found himself hoping that he didn't encounter that particular student again. He had never admitted even to himself that he was disappointed in this University and now he felt ashamed. While talking business with the Comptroller he was strangely detached, he hardly listened, a far-away look was in his eyes. It was painful for Tyndall to admit to himself that all his sly, and witty comments about the University had been his method of concealing blandly from himself that he was disappointed in the place.

He had come from another country with his own private dream of Toronto. In what way had it really disappointed him? The question stuck in his mind; it still troubled him when he was coming downstairs on his way across the front campus to Simcoe Hall for a brief conference with the President, who had said jokingly that he had to be careful about coming into Hart House, for every time he crossed the threshold he was button-holed and told they needed a new door-mat or a hat-rack.

Passing the door of the reading-room and catching a glimpse of one of those group-of-seven Northern Landscapes that hang on the wall, Tyndall hesitated, frowned and turned back. The students sitting at the long tables and in the chairs around the

10

wall were surprised to see the Warden standing before this picture with a troubled air and studying it as if he had never seen it before.

Pictures like this one had built up his expectations of the country. He had dreamed of brooding northern landscapes. That first summer-time he had gone on a fishing trip to the north shore of Lake Superior and there in the blue Algoma hills had looked upon this sombre operatic country and felt its remote loneliness, and had seen the great hills rising like cathedrals against the slashes of light made by the setting sun. In the loneliness he had found grandeur. The whole countryside, the northland, the prairies, the deep rivers, accentuated in his mind his belief that in such a land and among its people there would be a poetry, a wildness or a harsh strength. He had seemed to hear the music of Sibelius. Even the extremes of climate, the unbearably hot summers and the fiercely cold winters, suggested an extreme of character in the people, a vigour, a passion. But in this city and at this university he had felt only a dismal lack of passion. Even among the students who should be so alive and so open to intellectual stimulation, and among the Faculty men, too, he had found a peculiar mildness and a lack of true affability and charm. As a city Toronto had a reticent coldness. In other Ontario towns and in the West they jeered at Toronto. But he had soon learned that many of these places were simply smaller Torontos. The more bitterly they mocked at Toronto the more conscious they seemed to be that the Toronto spirit was a skeleton hidden in their own closets.

Sighing, he turned away from the picture and went out. No one would have known that he was troubled, for as he came out of Hart House he began to smile and bow with his familiar aplomb. There on the drive was Professor Brett, of the Philosophy Department, a man with an orderly mind who had

11

written a textbook on psychology. And coming up the road by U. C. was Professor J. C. McLennan, who had done distinguished work with the British Admiralty. Some people said he was the best-dressed man in Toronto. "How do you do, sir." And then, "Still fine weather, sir," Tyndall called out.

It was the hour when Hart House is emptying, when the walk leading south past University College is crowded with men and girls, and over to the left on the paths through the park come the students from Victoria and St. Mike's, and on the front campus they are wandering in groups toward the library, the School of Science, the Physics building, or the Mining building down on College Street. Today all of them seemed to Tyndall so much better dressed than the students in Paris, or the students at any of the English universities with the exception of Oxford and Cambridge. And the girls were so much prettier.

Walking more slowly than usual Tyndall began to cross the campus heading for Simcoe Hall, that Georgian building adjoining Convocation Hall. As he stopped to light his pipe he looked into the faces of these healthy students, asking himself what it was that he missed in the life around there. The students who didn't come from Toronto came from places with names like Galt and Guelph, Hornepayne and Sudbury and Walkerville and Owen Sound. Each one of them came with a little dream of his own; all of them nursed their dreams and waited for this big university to do something to their lives. Well, what did it do?

Down there was the Medical building, and across the road the red brick School of Practical Science; then the Mining building and, across that other road leading to College Street, the Physics building; and in a wide circle around this little neighbourhood were the Arts colleges. All these places were like separate fields of knowledge. It was a little world. Yet no: how could it be a remote little world when it was a source of the most powerful currents in modern civilization? In those buildings and in the minds of those well-dressed students loafing across the campus in the October sunlight were the ideas that made the whole of modern life what it was. From the little red school house came the technicians, from the Medical School the doctors, and from the labs the research men; and the teachers of philosophy were there, expressing the ideas men lived by. It all added up to a picture of our technological civilization. What happened there and what happened in the minds of students was important to everybody in the country. It didn't matter if the factory worker couldn't see it, or if the miner in Northern Ontario wasn't aware of it, or if the stenographer on Bay Street thought her life untouched by it. Day by day the lives of millions of people in the country could be altered by what happened in those buildings.

Tyndall had forgotten to light his pipe, the match had burned his fingers and he stood rooted to the one spot, reaching eagerly in his mind for an elusive perception.

If what happened here was important to the way men lived, he thought, walking on slowly, then clearly a man could say, "Does all this knowledge in all these fields teach us how to live?" Was there any design to it all? Had the University any character of its own? If a university shaped the lives of millions of people who never got beyond grade school it ought to shape the lives of its own men, its own students. A man ought to be able to recognize a way of life in the students and teachers. There ought to be some pattern to all these separate fields of knowledge, a pattern, which made a recognizable imprint on the men and women who came there.

But he had never been able to recognize the imprint. He had never been able to see the pattern as a whole, and the plain truth was that there was no imprint, no pattern. And the lives of the students acquired no Toronto tone or character . . . .

Delighted by his rich perceptions, which were such a satisfactory rational explanation of his disappointment in the place, he went on more briskly to Simcoe Hall. He had great confidence in his own judgment. His mind was at ease. Passing Knox, the Presbyterian Divinity College, there like a massive impenetrable fortress of weathered blue stone, he thought, "I've never been in there. I wonder what goes on in there?" and he smiled to himself.

That night, when he was alone in his own quarters, he stood for a long time with his elbow on the dresser, looking at the photograph of Phyllis Hallam. It was a good picture of Phyllis. He liked the three-quarter angle of the face, the soft dreaminess of the eyes, the thick black hair parted on the side, and the tilt of the round firm chin. And as he stared at the photograph, Phyllis herself seemed to be there beside him in her pale blue dress, and it was as if he were about to offer her a little gift which would draw them closer together.

Phyllis had never wanted him to come to Toronto. He could see now that she had been right. His Toronto plan had been made before he and Phyllis had thought of spending their lives together.

The life they had shared had been so brief; it had really begun only a year and a half ago in Europe, during the summer when both of them had been on a holiday in Paris. It was true that he had known the Hallams for some years in Wellington, where J. C. Hallam was an investment banker. But the Hallams had a lot more money than he had: he and Phyllis hadn't spent much time together. Then, too, she was the younger of the two by eight years. That June afternoon in Paris, while he was in Brentano's book shop, he had heard a girl's voice coming from behind a stack of books. She was asking the salesman for *The Dove's Nest*, by Katherine Mansfield. Tyndall had been able to see only the line of her shoulder in the pale blue dress, and the black hair at her neck. Moving towards her quietly until he was right behind her, he had whispered suddenly: "I believe Katherine Mansfield is also a New Zealander." Startled, she had turned and then cried, "Why, Arthur! Imagine! What are you doing here?" As she put out both her hands they had started to laugh in unison, and perhaps they knew then that they were going to spend a lot of time together.

Then had followed those three wonderful weeks, the days successively becoming more remarkable, as they kept on asking each other how it was they hadn't really got to know each other in New Zealand. They seemed to have read the same books. Now they wanted to go to the same places. They had begun to take long walks in the neighbourhood of the little art galleries near the Senate, and they often got lost; but she had an instinct for heading in the right direction and so she would lead the way. On the cobblestone streets she had worn the lifts off her heels. They had played golf out at St. Cloud, and he really played a fine game of golf. But when they had played tennis on the enclosed tan-bark courts she had beaten him easily, and had jeered at the way he made futile motions with his wrists and at his explanation: "The wrist motion in golf is not the same as in tennis. I'm out of practice in tennis. That's all, Phyllis."

And how happy they had been on those nights when they wandered down from the right bank and stood on the Pont St. Michel watching the reflection of the lights in the river, then went slowly up the Boul. Mich. trying to pick out the café where Oscar Wilde might have sat. And afterwards they had always rested in the Café des Lilas on Montparnasse, not far away from the Observatoire, which they had made their own café. In the late spring it had always been lovely there, with the statue of Marshal Ney rising among the leaves of the chestnut trees, and the street musicians coming to stand under the trees and play their songs for the patrons. At that café he had asked Phyllis to marry him. It had all been so unpremeditated, too. Phyllis had been having dinner with her father and she was to meet him at the Lilas where he had been waiting with that fat and fantastic Willi Polder, an Austrian whom he had known at Oxford and who had the conviction that he was going to die of a heart attack within a couple of years and so was inviting the world to share his final outburst of happiness. After beating Willi in a game of billiards he had come out to the terrace to look for Phyllis, and had seen her standing there shyly as if afraid to sit down by herself. Because she felt shy and alone, she was trying to look unapproachably proud and independent. While apologizing to her for not being on the terrace he had suddenly faltered, looked at her with an air of grave approval, and asked her to marry him. It had all come so easily and naturally.

He had talked to her about going to Canada, of course, but then, they had talked of so many places. He hadn't told her that he had definitely accepted a position as Warden of Hart House, at the University of Toronto. He had put off telling her about it until the next night, when they were back at the Lilas.

"I thought it was only a vague plan," she said unhappily. "You should have told me it was a definite arrangement, Arthur."

"Until now," he protested, "it seemed to be something far away from you and me."

"But why go off to Canada?"

"It sounded attractive, Phyllis. It would be interesting. You'd like it. I know you'd like it."

"Would I? Well, I thought that you . . . well, with my father in Wellington . . . it would be so easy to . . ." She broke off

16

and stood up slowly. The dream she had been making had vanished. She was all mixed up and unreasonably angry. "You'll hate it," she whispered. "I know you'll hate it," and she turned away abruptly and hurried off along Montparnasse.

As she passed under the first street light, a slim girl in a pale blue dress, hurrying so fast that she kept breaking her stride, he felt such an emptiness in his heart that he couldn't stir. Then suddenly he rushed after her. "Phyllis!" he cried out, wildly.

As she turned, the desolation in his face must have shocked her, for she shook her head but couldn't speak; then she put out her hand to him, and they were both shy and bewildered by their own emotion. Without saying anything they began to walk along the Boulevard. Finally she said quietly, "I was being selfish, Arthur. I should go where you planned to go." It seemed then that they only wanted to agree about everything. But even while they were arranging that he would go to Toronto and she would follow later if he liked it in Toronto, he was still bewildered by the emotion he had felt as he had followed after her blindly: at that moment he had known that he would have to go on following her, known that it didn't matter where they went so long as they were together.

Well, she had been reasonable and yielding, and he had come to Toronto, and here he was now in his own quarters, telling himself that his thoughts would delight and amuse her.

Then he sat down to write her a letter. It was time for him to make an honest decision, he wrote. Toronto had been a big disappointment and he had tried with a cynical cheerfulness to conceal it from himself. It wasn't his idea of a university at all. It was a big factory. A facts factory. It had no tone. It made no mark of its own on anybody. It was time to be honest with himself and he knew his life would be wasted there. The place had no atmosphere, no colour, no flair.

It had been hard for him to write this part of the letter but from then on he began to enjoy himself. It was as if he had been secretly nursing a contempt for this university for a whole year. Now he slashed into it. A state or provincial university was pretty much of a big impersonal machine without any tone anyway, he wrote, but here the pattern was more complicated and so broken into little pieces. It made no cultural sense at all, for here were Arts colleges called Victoria, a Methodist college; Trinity, an Anglican college; and St. Michael's, a Catholic college; and University College which was undenominational.

Chuckling to himself he wrote: "Do you remember when we used to read those books on Psychology and Psychiatry and how we used to talk about split personalities? Do you remember that strange case we read about, a girl named Doris, who didn't just have a split personality, but a multiple personality? There was Sleeping Doris, and Real Doris, and Laughing Margaret and Margaret, all in the one sick personality and all emerging separately at times to take over the life of the poor patient and bewilder the doctor. Well, think of this big university as a sick personality called George: Pious George goes to St. Michael's, Laughing Cynical George goes to University College, Complacent Comfortable George goes to Trinity, Evangelical George goes to Victoria, and Dumb Practical George goes to the School of Practical Science; and not all the psychiatrists in the Medical School can ever put George together so that he can come out into the sunlight as one real personality.

"So we'll forget our little plan of having you come to Toronto. I'll arrange decently to leave here at the end of the year and come home, and you might ask your father to look around and use his influence."

Much pleased with himself and feeling like an honest man he sealed his letter and looked around the room. He looked for those things which he had brought with him to Toronto. On the book-shelf was a death mask of the poet, John Keats. In a case on the lower shelf was a silver flute that had been his father's. Taking the flute from the case he began to play, sitting by the window and dreaming of the wide Wellington harbour and the great range of hills rising to the sky. He played to himself for an hour; then it began to rain and he jumped up and closed the window.

CHAPTER TWO

UT at the end of the week unfortunately he went to the Varsity-Queen's football game at the Bloor Street Stadium. In the old covered stand on Devonshire Place he sat with the athletic director and a prominent lawyer who had once captained a Varsity team. It was a clear fine day, a little too warm to be good football weather, but just right for the ladies who came to the college game beautifully dressed and took the walk around the cinder track to their seats in the open concrete stands. In those open stands the hats and coats and dresses of the women in the sunlight were a blaze of autumn colours. Everybody in town who can get a seat comes to the college games. It is always a happy well-dressed crowd. People seem to enjoy just being there as much as they do the game itself. They like the cavorting cheer leaders, the bands, the college songs, the defiant yells of the Meds, the "toike oike" of the engineers and the general horseplay. The cheering rises and rolls and rumbles for miles across the city.

23

That autumn Varsity had a pretty good team, with big Warnie Snyder being as good as he ever was, but it was about a year away from being a championship team, and Queen's, with Leadley and Batstone, fielded about the best team they ever had.

Then the sun had dipped beyond the Observatory building, leaving a kind of glowing mist over the field. Queen's had won. Their students were forming a snake line for a dance along Bloor Street. The crowd from the open stands was streaming across the field.

Having left his companions Tyndall came down to the cinder track and turned to watch the crowd straggling along. A particular spectator attracted his attention. Coming toward him was this plump healthy citizen with a flushed face, a brown felt hat on the back of his head. He was a little gray at the temples. He carried a blanket and his topcoat on his arm. He wore an expensive fawn-coloured jacket. Around his neck was a bright plaid scarf which dangled in the breeze. His expression was opulent, his face glowed with vast good will. He had the happy careless step, the sparkle of elation in his eye. He had all the bonhomie of a speculator on the grain exchange who had just made a million dollars. But he looked like a sublime caricature of the happy old graduate. It was the plaid scarf worn with such negligent grace that made Tyndall start to chuckle. Suddenly he recognized the man; he was a lawyer whom Tyndall had met at a dinner at the York Club.

"Hello there, Mr. Hicks," he called out.

"Why, hello, Tyndall," the lawyer said stopping. "Great game, wasn't it? I don't mind losing that one."

"Very good. Very exciting and rather heart-breaking, Hicks."

"Great broken field running in that last quarter. A fine team this year. What do you think, Tyndall?"

"Do you want to know what I was really thinking?" Tyndall asked, still chuckling as he lit his pipe. "I was admiring you as you crossed the field. At first I didn't recognize you. I wondered who you were. You looked so happy, so wonderfully alive. All by yourself you were a procession of the triumphant old graduates. It's a wonderful thing when a football game can give a man such a glow. Providing, of course, that it was the football game," he added significantly.

"Nonsense, Tyndall. It wasn't just the game," the lawyer protested earnestly. "Why, I feel like this every time I come here. Wouldn't miss this walk across the field for anything."

"The walk across the field. But why?"

"I always walk across the field. Ghosts, Tyndall."

"Ghosts?"

"Exactly, Tyndall," the lawyer said, looking around the field, all shadowed now by the covered stands, with the mist settling, the air getting heavier and cooler. But the lawyer did not look at all like a haunted man. Putting on his overcoat he linked his arm under Tyndall's, saying, "Which way are you walking?"

"Toward Hart House. Going that way, Hicks?"

"I'm parked down there. I'll walk with you," he said cheerfully. Striding along, with the little grin on his red face, his eyes were strangely tender.

"What's this about ghosts?" Tyndall asked, falling in step with him.

"It may be hard for you to understand."

"But it sounds interesting. Go on."

"After all you've only been around here a year, Tyndall."

"I think I've got pretty close to things around here," Tyndall said complacently.

"It goes back much farther than the life around here," the lawyer explained with an airy wave in the direction of the back campus which they were approaching. "In fact it goes right back to the time when we were kids." Smiling to himself he marched

25

along, happy with his own thoughts, not saying a word for some twenty paces. "Next door to the house in which I lived," he said finally, "there was a vacant lot. Two little kids about nine years old used to play there with a football. One would get about twenty feet away from the other and yell 'I'm Jack Maynard', and the other would yell, 'And I'm Hugh Gall', and then the kid with the ball would charge across the lot and try to elude the tackle of the other little kid. Well, one day the kid with the ball was brought down heavily by the other kid who smeared him in the mud and sat there on top of him. The kid who was in the mud lived in a house across the street. The door of this house opened and the kid's grandmother, who had been watching at the window, shouted angrily, 'Johnny! Get up off Pete. Get up and leave him alone, you little bully. You're two inches taller than Pete is. Get up and leave him alone, you coward, or I'll tell your mother.' Johnny got up slowly and backed away. But Pete, still holding the ball against his little chest, his face all muddy, jumped to his feet and screamed, 'He's not doing anything to me, Granny. I'm Jack Maynard, don't you hear, and he's Hugh Gall and this is the Varsity Stadium. Why don't you go in and leave us alone?'"

The lawyer who had been smiling innocently to himself as he told this story now grew a little embarrassed. "Well, Tyndall, those two kids of course go on to high school, they come with their fathers to watch the college games. If their high school teams get into the finals they play at the Stadium. All over the city, maybe all over Ontario there are thousands of kids dreaming of that stadium. Oh, well, I'm afraid I don't make myself clear. Sound sentimental, don't I? Sorry, Tyndall. Great game though, wasn't it? Well, here's my car. Nice seeing you. Have to hurry. Meeting my wife at a party. So long."

"Just a minute," Tyndall called. "What was your college?"

"Victoria. Why?"

"Oh, I was just wondering. So long, Hicks."

"So long, Tyndall," called the lawyer, and getting into his car he drove away leaving Tyndall standing there by the iron fence on Hoskin. The crowd wandering down the street brushed against him as he walked slowly toward Hart House. But he had the hesitant reluctant step of a man who was aware that he was walking away from a place where he had missed something. With a glance at his wrist watch he finally stopped. He knew that his curiosity was prompting him to do a foolish thing. Yet he turned, assuring himself that he was merely taking a little walk to stretch his legs before dinner, and he walked back to the Stadium gate which was still open. It was a little while before he could make up his mind to go in. But finally he entered and walked along the cinder path in the shadow of the open stand and sat down not far away from the place where he had watched the game, and there he smoked his pipe and pondered and stared at the fields and the stands as if he had never seen them before. Deserted and empty, with the action and the tumult gone, they looked bare and cold. The street lights along Bloor came on. Tyndall stayed there puffing his pipe as if waiting for someone. He wanted to see that field and the whole Stadium as the lawyer had seen it. He was trying to assess the richness of the lawyer's recollections of Varsity and to weight them against the thinness of his own impression revealed so cheerfully to Miss Hallam in the letter he had written.

To him the place had seemed to have no tradition, no substance of a tradition, although sometimes the shadow of an ancient alien tradition fell across the place. The lawyer probably never used the word tradition. Yet Varsity for him in his daily life was a living past. He had a good memory of things and those things had become woven into his life. And the ghosts?

27

Yes, the ghosts. Tyndall could see what he had meant. Staring at the field he believed for a moment that he could see it through the lawyer's eyes. It became alive for him. And those names of the college heroes, which had been just names he had read in the records, became the names of living men. And they didn't belong now simply to the University. They seemed to come running on to the playing field, out of the life of the whole Ontario community. There they were, the men who as kids had dreamed of the place, who had possessed a little piece of it while at high school, suddenly and exultantly making it belong completely to them. And those graduates, who had taken the same steps one by one toward the Stadium, now that the game had ended, came walking across the field. Fat, mellow and graying, they strode along, their feet sinking into the cleat marks on the field, and in their imagination there flitted past them, not just the charging figures they had seen that day, but the figures of all those players whose names had been so important to them in the past. They all came thudding by in the twilight with the mist settling and the damp smell coming from the field. They were all ghosts, but in that company swirling around in the graduate's imagination were his boyhood chums, the ones he had grown up with at college, and those who suffered and struggled with him and sometimes failed. It was a march of ghosts on that field, opening up his whole past and making it seem good and moving.

How odd it was, Tyndall thought, that an opulent old graduate, a Victoria man, should have impressed this on him so vividly.

It had got much cooler, the air was damp and thick. Shivering, Tyndall stood up. "How odd. How very odd," he said aloud. Then he began to hurry toward the south entrance. But the gate was closed. It was ridiculous, but he was locked in the Stadium. For a few moments he looked at the gate, smiled to himself, looked around furtively, gripped his pipe in his teeth and hoisted himself up and over the gate and dropped lightly onto the cement. He looked around again and grinned like a schoolboy. He began to hurry toward Hart House.

As he passed the porter's desk in the front hall he turned suddenly to the Comptroller, who was there behind the desk reading a letter. The Comptroller, a big fellow with a soft gentle voice, liked managing the business details of Hart House.

"By the way," Tyndall said, approaching the desk, "you've been around here a long time, haven't you?"

"Why, yes, Mr. Tyndall. What's on your mind?"

"It just occurred to me. If you were asked about this place one of the first things you'd say would be 'No ghosts'. Isn't that right?"

"No ghosts! I don't follow you," the Comptroller said looking closely at the Warden.

"I mean, little sense of the past. Do students ever say to themselves, 'Here on these paths walked the famous So-and-so. Right out there a prime minister led a student's strike. The poet So-and-so sat on these steps.' Do I make myself clear, old man?"

"I think so. Well, yes," the Comptroller agreed. "Not many ghosts."

"But you might be wrong," Tyndall said enigmatically. And while the Comptroller looked more puzzled than ever Tyndall asked suddenly, "Do you think you'd be able to single out a Victoria man?"

"Oh, I think so," the Comptroller said dubiously. "A Victoria man more easily than the others. He might be more earnest, I suppose."

"Yes, I think so," Tyndall agreed. "Well, cheerio," and he smiled to himself, giving the bewildered Comptroller no satisfaction at all. But the fact was, Tyndall thought, that the old graduate with his good memories had been a Victoria man.

29

Maybe Victoria had put its imprint on him. Maybe each of the colleges left an unforgettable imprint on a man. Maybe they also gave him an intellectual pattern. It was possible he had missed something. The poet, Ned Pratt, of the English Department at Victoria, had invited him to his home where he had hearty stag parties. They had also played a game of golf together. He liked Pratt. The poet had a nice muscular gaiety in his work and in his character and he played a good game of golf. "I'll suggest a game of golf and he may ask me over there to Victoria to have lunch with him," Tyndall thought.

CHAPTER THREE

HE mild weather lasted over the weekend. There was a lot of sunlight at noontime on Monday when Tyndall came up the little slope from the crescent to Victoria. There was the brownstone main building with its one pointed tower. Architecturally that main building seems to have come out of the dream that was responsible for the heavy brown sobriety of the Parliament Buildings at the other end of the park. The fact has a certain political interest. Now the main building is flanked by Burwash Hall, the men's residence, gray stone Gothic with a lighter touch; and to the left, on Avenue Road, by the severely chaste library.

Before the federation of the colleges Victoria had been a university itself at Cobourg. Victoria men liked to make this fact clear at once to a stranger like Tyndall. Nor had Victorian administrators rushed eagerly to Toronto and federation with the wind in their hair and their arms outstretched. The keepers of the powerful Methodist conscience, they had no intention of accepting Bishop Strachan's Anglican vision as the State pattern for education. That old Victorian Chancellor, who became Superintendent of Education in Ontario, held a watching brief over his Victoria's destiny; from his place in heaven and in biography he probably still does. But later, Chancellor Burwash, a milder man, had welcomed the federation in calmer political weather. Victoria used to draw most of its students from the little Ontario towns. As time passes and residential life becomes more expensive and Toronto high school students come in greater numbers it tends to become truly a Toronto college.

The slopes were still surprisingly green, and in the sunlight students were sprawled on the grass. On the playing field on Charles Street others were kicking a football around. Girls in bright coats and dresses were like pigeons on the grass in that little corner between the tennis court and Burwash Hall.

The Faculty room on the ground floor is like a small edition of that room in Hart House. It opens onto the handsome dining-room with big windows and shafts of sunlight. After lunch you can return to the Faculty room for coffee. Tyndall had lunch with Ned Pratt, who unfortunately had one early lecture right after lunch, so Tyndall was left sitting with a plump pink-cheeked, white-haired professor of philosophy and a younger freckled, sandy-haired, slight young man of the English Department. Sitting at the end of the table by the southern window Tyndall began to question them gently and unobtrusively, as if he hoped to catch them off balance, and the two Victoria men, one sitting on the table, the other standing with his arm on the back of Tyndall's chair, were affability itself. They enjoyed having him there.

"I've been around here more than a year," Tyndall said apologetically, "but I sometimes feel I haven't got the true picture of any of these colleges very clear in my head. One has to live in them, don't you think? Although I suppose I'd be safe in assuming that nearly every student in that dining-room had a Methodist background."

"Well, no, not necessarily," said the pink-cheeked philosopher.

"But his faith would be important, wouldn't it?"

"I suppose it might be asked of him when he registered. Yes, it might."

"But supposing a student said frankly he was an atheist or had no religion at all?"

"Oh that!" said the thin, freckled younger one with a shrug. "I think that has happened around here, hasn't it, Will?"

"Of course, I'm sure it has."

"But why would he come here?"

"Why, maybe something he liked about Victoria. Yes, the tradition of freedom, of independence of thought," said the English professor simply.

"But really . . ."

"Yes, a sense of liberty," the older went on with an approving smile. "The fact that a man might believe what he wanted to believe while he was a student here. Don't you agree, Henry?"

"I think that's a fair statement."

"Oh, come now," Tyndall protested good-naturedly. "Surely your Board of Governors would object if their Christian college was crowded to the rafters with little atheists and hottentots. What if they made noisy gestures rejecting the faith of their fathers? Oh, you must admit there would be an objection."

"Oh, sooner or later something would be said," agreed the younger man.

"Yes, there might be an objection," the white-haired professor agreed with a happy chuckle. "The objection, however, would probably come in the form of innumerable letters from supporters of the college. You see—from outside the college."

35

Growing more serious, he went on, "You see, Tyndall, the old Methodist tradition gets into the blood. It's there when the young don't realize it's there. We often see interesting manifestations of this spirit. As you know, that great old tradition depends on the individual conversion, the change of heart, the change of direction. And, of course, sometimes in a student it works in reverse. It's the old story, Tyndall: if a student's parents have been unyieldingly severe as Christians then the student finds himself wanting to reject all he's supposed to accept. The fling at the moon, Tyndall. The individual trip to Cathay. But he makes his own choice. Of course, he may return later on. Oh, we see it happening all the time. It's almost a tradition around here."

"Then too," put in the younger one, "if the place was full of atheists there might be a feeling that the Christian spirit of the teachers wasn't very persuasive," and he smiled blandly at his friend.

"Hm," the Warden said doubtfully. "Then the Lord only knows who is apt to be registered here." He looked baffled, but they both were still patient and reasonable.

"Oh, quite so," they agreed.

"Tell him about the eminent psychologist, Will."

"No, that mightn't be wise. It wouldn't be fair."

"Well, don't mention his name. Go on, Will."

"Yes, do go on," Tyndall said eagerly.

"He's so well known," the philosopher said. "And, of course, he mightn't want to admit this publicly, but it's the way we tell the story anyway." His face was all wrinkled up in a warm smile and his friend nodded eager approval, too. "Well, Tyndall, the story is that this eminent gentleman,—a Catholic, mind you, by birth and intention at the time—came to the University from out of town. By mistake he registered at Victoria College. I won't say that he thought he was registering at St. Michael's. He may have been one of those Catholics who go to U. C. But the point is that he was a Catholic. He didn't notice that he was within the Methodist citadel. In fact nobody ever seemed to call it to his attention, and so we don't know if he ever really became aware of it. Perhaps it got that he liked the place and didn't care, but he went on and completed his course here. Some day I'll introduce you to him and you can ask him about it yourself."

They both enjoyed this story very much, but Tyndall laughed and looked frustrated.

"What I'd like to ask him is if he doesn't think that the Board of Governors would object. If this Protestant college were crowded with Catholics wouldn't there be a lot of eye-raising somewhere?"

"Oh, there would be more than a fluttering of the brows," they agreed cheerfully. "But we don't think it would result in a religious test for applicants."

"It's all so — so — well, so liberal," Tyndall said unhappily.

"Exactly. Exactly. Why should that puzzle you, Tyndall?"

"Well, let's put it this way," the Warden said, as if he felt that they were evading him. "What chance is there of a professor being kicked out for his lack of orthodoxy? How often does it happen?"

"How often? Well, it's a question of whether it ever happened."

"Ah, then it did happen."

"Oh, that's a question," they agreed. They smiled deprecatingly. They suddenly chuckled. They had a little private joke. The Warden waited and felt as baffled as if he was in Tibet asking silly but serious questions of some Lama who wanted to be patient and charitable no matter how preposterous he found them.

"But if there was one man," the Warden insisted.

"Well, yes, one man was asked to leave, I believe," said the young freckled-faced one. "And he was unorthodox—but it's a question of the direction in which his unorthodoxy lay, isn't it, Will?"

"Yes, that's a neat way of putting it, Henry."

"He was in philosophy, I presume."

"Oh, my goodness, no. The languages."

"But that's hardly a controversial field. I don't understand."

"Let's see now. It is as if this nameless one made himself most unorthodox."

"Yes," chuckled the English professor. "There are some who insist that he was a most unorthodox pipe smoker. He blew great clouds of smoke around the place. Yes, a powerful pipe can become a powerful challenge. Extremely unorthodox, do you see, Tyndall?"

"I see. Then there was no heresy . . ."

"Well, rather a question of the unorthodox personal gesture. It was complicated. Very complicated."

"I see," said the Warden. "Yes, I see." But now he really wanted to find a crack, a flaw in the impenetrable and beautifully tolerant liberal breastwork which these men had such faith in. All his own impressions of their college had been false and misguided.

"Let me be right about something," he pleaded with a genial grin. "Let me go on believing that Victoria, for whatever it is, will become more and more what Toronto is."

"Oh, I think that's fair, accurate," the younger one said.

"And it's not really so embarrassing, Tyndall. These students from the Toronto high schools are pretty good stuff."

"And remember also that Toronto changes from decade to decade."

"Good," Tyndall said. "I think, too, that Victoria would represent that progressive liberal class. The powerful Canadian or Toronto middle class—"

"Just a minute, Tyndall," said the plump pink-faced professor, his whole face lighting up as he leaned closer. "Let's put it this way, Tyndall. You want to know what Victoria stands for, eh? And what it is willing to defend? Well, I'll tell you. The semi-underprivileged. Have you got it? Not the underprivileged. The semi-underprivileged." Leaning back he chuckled deeply and his colleague also grinned cheerfully. But Tyndall didn't know whether they were jibing at the college or jeering at him. And it put him in a cynical mood.

"I see your point. It is a good one. And I suppose the dominant intellectual influence here is also in the best progressive North American tradition. Do the students all read John Dewey?"

"Dewey. Why, Dewey?"

"He's got us confused with U. C."

"But you take a certain pragmatic view of things yourselves, gentlemen. I thought it might be Dewey."

"I wouldn't say anybody around here reads Dewey," the older one said. "Would you, Henry?"

"No, it hadn't occurred to me, Will."

"Me, neither."

"Well, surely there must be some philosopher who seems to represent the goal, the intellectual influence of the college," Tyndall insisted, wanting to pin them down.

"Well, I think there is," the young one agreed.

"But who?"

"Why, Plato," he said calmly. "Wouldn't you say Plato, Will?"

"Yes, Plato. Yes, of course, Plato. That's as close as you could come to it."

"Plato," Arthur Tyndall repeated. He smiled. It was a bland, charming, cynical smile that concealed his frustration. Then Ned Pratt came in, smiling happily, his overcoat pockets filled with golf balls, and Tyndall shook hands with the others.

On the way out Tyndall was muttering to himself. "Plato and Toronto. Toronto and Plato." And if he went over to St. Mike's and asked for a magical name that would reveal the intellectual scheme of that place they would probably say, "St. Thomas Aquinas." And University College would also, no doubt, say "Plato." And Trinity! Well, what did it tell him? What was the use? It was all Toronto. And yet nothing was really revealed to him. All his impressions about Victoria had been false. It was not a Puritan, not even a Methodist, college. The men who had answered his questions had been sincere and straightforward. No one was deliberately misleading him.

A stubborn expression came on his face as he slung his bag of golf clubs over his shoulder. Turning he looked at the main brownstone building, and he raised his eyebrows. It seemed to him that he had been brushed aside as he tried to peer under a mask. It was possible also that in his year at this university he had encountered only the one vast mask. What if all his impressions had been wrong? What if he had never really seen beneath the mask? What if the place had a tone, an atmosphere, and the thing that might have revealed it was hidden, yet possible of discovery? When his curiosity was really aroused, Tyndall was a determined man.

As they went down the path that tall dark-haired girl with the round face and dark eyes, Helen Winston, who was now sitting on the grass with a good-looking blonde girl, called out cheerfully, "Hello, Mr. Tyndall."

"Why, er . . . Hello," Tyndall said, staring at her blankly. He was preoccupied with his problem, and so irritated that he had no recollection of ever having seen her before. She was just a Victoria girl in a brown tweed overcoat and a fawn-coloured sweater.

CHAPTER FOUR

T WOULD never have occurred to Helen Winston, of Regina, that she and Arthur Tyndall were on the same intellectual adventure, both feeling suddenly the impact of multiple fields of knowledge in a university that was like an unknown country. Nor would she have believed that during her years at Victoria, Plato was about to become the philosophical influence on her life. When she smiled at Tyndall, he reminded her of Hart House and she wondered, a little resentfully, why women were excluded from its cloistered corridors.

She was still in the first uneasy rapture of her life in residence at Annesley Hall. It had been a jolt like the emptying of her heart to be shown for the first time the small room she was to share with another student. The sight of this room seemed to wrench her painfully away from her own home, for it was unfurnished, the walls bare, the beds just naked frames. If it was to become a home, she and the girl who shared it with her, the blonde girl, Nancy Willson, who had been sitting on the grass with her when Tyndall passed, had to touch it with their own light and their own warmth and their own flair for decoration.

Then there had been the bewilderment of so many strange faces at breakfast and her recognition of the fact that some girls had so much more assurance than others. She had hoped that she smiled with a cool poise, but she felt shy and alone. And from the first day the phone had begun to ring and there were some girls who seemed to have come there simply to answer the phone. In those days, under Miss Addison, there were only three late leaves a week. The residence rules were just beginning to be "liberalized", as they say around Victoria nowadays.

But almost magically she got used to the new faces. Everything began to fall easily into the residence routine.

Helen, the daughter of a lawyer, was a scholarship student. Her room-mate, Nancy Willson, was a rich girl from Brantford. Living in the east Nancy had often come to Toronto and of course she felt wise, smooth, sophisticated and like a big sister of Helen's. That night Nancy was sitting on her bed eating an apple which she was slicing into neat sections. She had a proud and worldly air. At Victoria she felt already that she was ahead of her time. She had good clothes and a bright patter. She was three inches shorter than Helen whom she considered to be physically too formidable for smartness.

Sitting at the desk Helen was writing a letter home and trying to tell her father how she had felt that night they called "Freshie Night" at Annesley Hall. As she wrote the singing was still in her ears, and she smiled to herself. The men had all sung "Let Me Call You Sweetheart", and she would never forget it. Fitting into residence life, she wrote, had been both easy and complicated; for the one routine was being imposed upon her, with her background of Prairie life, and upon Miss Willson, with her pattern of life at Brantford. Each had her own home and her own past. Yet in a little while all were supposed to have something in common so that a stranger would know that they came from Annesley Hall.

"Seen anybody you like at any of the lectures?" Nancy Willson asked with a little smile as she delicately nibbled at a slice of her apple.

"I don't seem to have had time to sort them out."

"Oh, you're not that slow, Helen."

"That's a funny thing," Helen said shyly. "In the town where I come from there's perhaps one eligible boy, one boy you'd want to go out with, one boy you fancy you might possibly marry some day, and then when you come here, well . . ."

"Well, what?"

"Well, there seem to be twenty boys all in the one lecture room. I mean boys who have the education, the interests, that you might share. At first it's a little bewildering and exciting, isn't it?" she asked, laughing apologetically. She did not want her innocent enthusiasm to appear ridiculous to Nancy. As soon as she had come to Annesley she had noticed Nancy. Most girls in their freshman year are awkwardly aware of girls like Miss Willson. These girls have a look of knowing about the latest fashion; they are aware of what is going on in the world. They know the fashion in books, in music and dancing. Their skirts are a little longer or a little shorter than those of the other girls. They speak with a nice intonation. For a whole year the girls from the smaller towns long to be as "smooth" as these girls. "Of course I don't mean I'm still excited," she added, not wanting to be taken for too simple a heart. "So far there don't seem to be many places to meet the men."

"Try the library."

"Yes, I've been in the library."

"You don't go to the library to read a book, silly. You go to look around and see who's there."

"Oh. Well, here's something, Nancy. The first week every one of the boys seems remarkable and distinctive but after the first week, well, they don't seem so remarkable any more."

"Oh, I don't know," Nancy drawled. "Wait till you go home for the summer and start comparing them with that friend of yours."

"I don't suppose I'll take much interest in him, will I?"

"And he'll think you're an intellectual snob," Nancy said gravely. After a little further meditation she said profoundly, "Helen, I think you make a mistake with your honour English course."

"But why?"

"I've got a cousin who was here for four years. She's explained the whole situation to me. She, too, went in for English—and heavily. Well, the men fought shy of her. Do you see, Helen? You don't want them to decide that you're the intellectual type. If they do it means they'll never take you out on Saturday nights. In fact, according to my cousin, some of them take a pretty firm attitude to university women anyway. To tell you the truth, Helen, I think my cousin feels emotionally frustrated. Oh, she's bright as a dollar, but I'm sure she's secretly bitter. It's an awful thing to go through college and have no fun. All she has to warm her heart with is her degree—and she knows it. I don't intend to become emotionally frustrated."

"Who says you will, Nancy?" And then with a surprising firmness she cried, "I'll never be emotionally frustrated around here. I feel too happy already."

"Such ardour, Helen. But I think you should wear your hair differently. Just think, this place is called Annesley Hall."

"Well, why not?"

"That was the name of Lord Byron's home. I suppose that's right," she said pondering. "There were always a lot of women in his home, weren't there? Or is it just an academic joke?"

"I don't really know," Helen said. Standing at the window and hardly listening, she was looking down at the lights of Avenue Road. Suddenly she felt happy. She had never felt this kind of happiness. Her face began to glow and her lips were parted. It was as if she were standing on the edge of a widening world that beckoned to her. A sense of expectancy suffused her whole being; when she was a small girl she used to want to whoop when she was happy. Yet this was not actually a physical happiness. It was like the sudden enlargement of her spirit, a brightening glow in her imagination; she could feel herself reaching out with all her mind and her heart toward those fields of knowledge now opening to her; there at the window she felt her life already widening. And she glowed with such a quiet happiness that Nancy, who had been watching her intently, asked, "What's the dream, Helen? Who is he?"

"Who is who?"

"What are you thinking about?"

"I was wondering when the debates would begin. Wouldn't it be lovely, Nancy, if we could get into the debates, the intercollegiate debates with the men? Only I guess a girl has no chance, eh, Nancy?"

"The debates! Is that what you were thinking? Oh my gosh!" And she burst out laughing.

CHAPTER FIVE

HE December days brought Indian Summer and those few mild days which follow the first snowfall. Snow powdered the campus in the morning, hoar-frost glistening on the weathered stone face of the old library building was gone with the first sunlight. The campus was wet and muddy and the students walked round it, keeping to the sidewalk. On such a morning Tyndall was walking toward the library with Professor H——, of the Philosophy Department.

Professor H——, the philosopher, always had an indulgent air when he walked with Tyndall. Of course he had an indulgent air with most people. He was about six-foot-two, slim shouldered and long-legged, and was a brilliant lecturer, greatly admired by his pupils. When he came into class he would ease himself toward the table, let his paunch rest comfortably on the table top, wipe his glasses, throw his head back and look down his long nose at the class with a kind of calculated innocent surprise. He, too, was a Platonist. He knew how to provoke a class. He had a mocking style and a good sharp mind; he could rip a student's argument to pieces, but he rarely revealed what he thought himself about life and death. If you could get him alone with no one listening, and he trusted you, he would answer a simple question directly and sincerely. He never made serious conversation when women were around, and he got invited to a lot of parties. He liked Tyndall, but usually he sparred with him, preferring the light touch. They were walking along in the sunlight, jesting with each other, and suddenly Tyndall came sneaking up on him with the kind of question he was beginning to ask everybody.

"Oh, by the way, I was wondering if you could say what distinguishes a man from the University of Toronto, let us say, from a Queen's man, a McGill man, or a Yale man, or a Michigan State man. Could you pick out a Toronto man by what you might call his intellectual pattern?"

"You mean as I could pick out a Yale man by the light in his eyes?"

"Exactly."

"Or a Harvard man by the circles under his eyes?"

"No, I'm serious."

"You mean has the Toronto man a way of life? It's too bad Maurice Hutton isn't around. You should ask him."

"Then you couldn't identify a Toronto Varsity man?"

"No, I don't think I could."

"But surely there must be some identification marks?"

"It's a big university, Tyndall, a big provincial university."

"And you couldn't recognize him?"

"No, I don't think I could, Tyndall. I don't think anyone else could either. But it's interesting. Maybe it's what's the matter with us around here. Off-hand I could only tell a Toronto man by his negative aspects. I could tell you what he isn't."

"Do go on. What are the negative aspects?"

"Well, he isn't very assertive, is he?"

"That's true, I've noticed it."

"And he isn't intellectually adventurous. He doesn't like to be thought queer in any way. No maverick, intellectually. A man who likes to fit into the accepted pattern. I should say also, Tyndall, that he's afraid of variety. Prefers the one mould."

"Ah, fine, and just how would you describe the mould?" Tyndall asked eagerly.

"Now, that's difficult. I can tell you what he isn't. I could tell you who he isn't but I couldn't tell you who he is."

"But you yourself are a product of Toronto, aren't you?"

"Me! That's different. Never tried to place myself, Tyndall. You take a shot at it," he said, brushing away the whole subject with an airy wave of his hand. He simply refused to talk about himself. It just wasn't done. The notion was appallingly embarrassing. "The Toronto man," he said chuckling. "A character in search of an author. You be the author, Tyndall. Well, I have to go into the library here. I have to wait in line and find that I can't get what I want. If you die with a million, Tyndall, why don't you leave it for a library? So long." And he went into the library with a happy little smile on his face.

But it seemed to Tyndall that the philosopher had neatly eluded him. One after another they all withdrew behind their masks. And this man illustrated the point perfectly. At a party one night he and Tyndall, withdrawing into a corner, had found themselves talking earnestly about the Christian religion. It had begun as a literary conversation about the Song of Solomon. And Tyndall had said innocently, "Of course you do believe in the resurrection, don't you?" And the professor, in the innocence of the moment, answered simply, "Yes, I do." Then suddenly a sophisticated lady who caught a snatch of the conversation cried,

"What's this? Upon my word! What's this about the resurrection?" And she burst into laughter. Others gathered around. The professor, blushing, and astonished at his betrayal of himself, mumbled some excuse, moved away, and ten minutes later left the party. He, a Toronto intellectual, had been close to declaring himself on an important matter. It was never done in Toronto. All men might have known him for what he was. "I mustn't ask these forthright questions," Tyndall thought. "They'll think I'm a little crazy. No one around here is crazy."

But his curiosity had become a habit of thought. One February afternoon in the bitter zero weather they held a convocation to award a degree to a prominent English visitor. Tyndall, of course, was at Convocation Hall. There was much handshaking and he was invited over to Government House to have tea the next day with the visitor. He had come out and was standing in the shelter of the big columns buttoning up his coat. He couldn't get used to the Canadian winters and the refusal of the Toronto natives to recognize that the days were unbearably cold. In Montreal men on the streets wore fur hats, some of the professors at McGill wore ski hats; but at this university few of the students wore long underwear. They simply ignored the zero weather.

A solidly built square-faced man came out with the tall Englishman, who looked very cold indeed. The solid man was the President, Sir Robert Falconer, whom Tyndall admired for his unobtrusive administrative abilities. The Englishman rushed ahead to the waiting car. Smiling at Tyndall the President hurried after him. Then Tyndall was joined by old Professor L——, the mathematician, who hadn't even buttoned up his coat.

"Going my way, Tyndall?" he asked cheerfully, and they fell in step.

The old mathematician was one of those men whom Tyndall

appreciated because he had that worldly touch which Tyndall did not associate with Toronto. What Tyndall didn't know was that the mathematician had lived all his life in Ontario. But he had the distinguished air, and a fine determination to be a character. He had a slightly affected precision of speech and a vast intellectual superiority that was very comforting. He handed out rebukes to his colleagues with a gentle smile and a condescending wit, and no one got angry at him. The rumour was that he was an atheist, but he was invited to the denominational colleges to recite poetry and talk about French literature and administer measured pontifical rebukes to those who questioned his judgment. Everybody enjoyed him because there was a knowing twinkle in his old blue eyes.

"For heaven's sake, button up your coat," Tyndall said as they started to cross the campus.

"Now come, Tyndall, you're young. You're warm-blooded," he said, drawing his coat together. The wind was howling across the bare snow-covered campus. It blew from the east across the park; the sky was leaden, and the turret of University College stuck up starkly cold against the sky. The wind seemed to hit the solid barrier of Knox College to the left, whirl, and catch up to the two figures plodding across the icy campus.

"Every time I pass Knox College I think I should go in there some time," Tyndall said.

"As a matter of fact I've never been in there myself. Go in and see the Principal some time. He's an amiable soul."

"He might think I wanted to know what went on in there."

"Oh, they're divinity men in there. They'd welcome you, Tyndall. Especially at this moment, poor fellow—you look half frozen."

"It's a violent climate for scholars," Tyndall said. "Sweltering sun in July and stinging cold in the winter. A violent climate for a violent people." Little puffs of steaming breath shot out of their mouths as they talked.

"Perhaps it's too cold for us to be violent," the mathematician said, chuckling. "On a day like this I have only one passion—to get beside a fire."

"But after all the Russians have a climate somewhat similar."

"Except that we're not Russians, Tyndall."

"Talking about passion, or extremes of temperament . . ."

"Were we, Tyndall?"

"It's something I've noticed, and maybe you've noticed the same thing yourself," Tyndall persisted. "Wouldn't you say there was a certain lack of passion around here—in the temperament of the students, the teachers, in us all?"

"Unfortunately, it's true, Tyndall. I think anyone would agree with you."

"It could be hidden, smouldering. It might break out in unexpected places."

"Gone underground, as it were, eh, Tyndall?"

"Something like that."

"But Tyndall, my dear fellow, what if there's no passion there at all?" the mathematician asked cheerfully.

"In that case there would be nothing but flatness," Tyndall said irritably, for it seemed to him that the portly mathematician was retreating as neatly as the philosopher had done. "And if so, it's a pity," he went on. "I remember the Canadian troops overseas, in London and in France. You could always tell a Canadian. And I've seen them on rampage. A wild and hearty roistering crew. Independent and reckless."

"My dear Tyndall," the mathematician said solicitously, "what's bothering you?"

"Nothing bothers me," Tyndall said quickly. But the professor's complacent solicitude annoyed him. "Why does it seem odd to you that I, working in a place, a cultural centre—I mean, never to see the direction it is taking, never to be aware of its tone, it's . . . it's . . . well, it's a form of deprivation, of enslavement."

"Tyndall, it's too big a place," the professor said soothingly. "Possibly we lack the bohemian touch a little. I don't mean the velvet jacket and La Bohème—I'm sure you follow me, don't you, Tyndall? The only place left for the bohemian is on the intellectual frontier. Possibly we are intellectually too middle-class. Possibly—yes, possibly. And as for passion, if you must have passion . . ." He had stopped suddenly by the east corner of University College and his eyes were twinkling merrily. "As you yourself surmised, Tyndall, a lot of passion around here may be secret." Pointing suddenly to an elderly professor, who had wheeled past them at the corner, his head down against the wind, his right hand holding up his coat collar, he said, "See that man there . . ."

"I've seen him a hundred times. He's in the English Department at U.C."

"A quiet, self-controlled citizen, you think, eh, Tyndall?"

"A bit of a recluse in his way, isn't he?"

"Yet he has a secret passion, Tyndall, a powerful secret passion," the mathematician said, reaching out and squeezing Tyndall's arm. "Such passions are dreadful things. Avoid them, Tyndall, avoid them. Good afternoon."

"Good afternoon," Tyndall said, following with his eyes the middle-aged man in the dark gray overcoat who was hurrying under the Gothic arch of the Memorial Tower. Tyndall had never had a conversation with this particular professor. All he knew about him was that he had a long nose, a bald head and fierce gray eyes, and was reputed to be an excellent teacher. For twenty years he had been at U.C. He held himself aloof from everybody. Nobody bothered with him.

But from that day on whenever he was in the Faculty room Tyndall watched this old professor with an absorbing curiosity. He hovered around him as if he were a rare object that he wanted to possess. He soon saw that this man had some secret obsession that made him a stranger among his colleagues. They avoided him and he knew it. He made no friendly gesture to anyone. He was gruff, lonely and sour. He ate alone. He walked alone to the lecture room. He had a habit of whipping his glasses out of the breast pocket of his coat, and Tyndall, watching furtively, detected a nervous tremble in the hand. In the Faculty room after lunch he would sit alone with a magazine, then lean back suddenly and close his eyes and cup his chin in his hand as if he were exhausted. But what had happened to the man? Tyndall asked himself. Why did he look like a frustrated old hermit? Whatever his weakness was, and the mathematician had said that he had a secret weakness, he clearly tried to conceal it. If he were alcoholic it would show in his eyes, although of course he might be a secret drinker. That would account for his dozing in the chair by the window. But he had strangely unyielding eyes. Years ago he might have had a sad and silly love affair. He might have made a fool of himself over some young woman and been ashamed of the scandal, and yet even now be unable to stop loving. There are so many ways in which a man can make a fool of himself and end up sitting alone.

Tyndall tried to draw close to him. He would sit down beside him, smile, and make casual conversation, and the bald professor would look surprised. He didn't try to discourage Tyndall. They talked about Dickens, Fielding, and Keats; and Tyndall was always watching and waiting to touch him suddenly on his old raw wound.

One night in University College there was a meeting of a body of citizens interested in adult education. Tyndall and the English professor met in the corridor. Then Principal Malcolm Wallace came by with a lawyer, a graduate of St. Michael's. Tyndall and his friend heard the graduate say, "I don't feel like a stranger here, Dr. Wallace. You see I used to take almost half my lectures in University College."

"You did no such thing," Dr. Wallace said with a sharp and surprising bluntness. "You mean that you took certain university subjects, possibly economic or history lectures, here, because it is the main building, and you had nothing whatever to do with U.C."

"Well, yes, of course, of course," the St. Michael's graduate said, looking embarrassed. "I see what you mean, Dr. Wallace. I should have thought of it in that way."

"There you are, Tyndall," the English professor grunted. "No matter where they come from they think they have a little mortgage on University College. Just because they have trampled all over the place."

"I see your point," Tyndall said politely. Of course a man is expected to have a special veneration for his own college, and University College had been the bastion on which the whole University had been built. When U.C. had been King's College, in the old days, it had stood there staunchly and defiantly while the tempests of envy and malice and resentment had swirled around it. It had felt all those pressures that tend to split an un-settled community life. In the beginning it was the realization of old Bishop Strachan's dream, an Anglican college, an Anglican dream; but the dream had blown up in the Bishop's face and he had moved on to Trinity, and the college without the old Bishop's dream to sustain it had become the godless college. And the godless, of course, are always at a disadvantage, because the more God-fearing feel entitled to raid and move in on them. U.C. had been left with its men who believed in the quest for the truth for truth's sake alone. And it had had notable teachers, like Maurice Hutton with his genius for making the classic world seem immediate and important, and Alexander and Milner and Dr. Wallace himself. "Of course the trouble is that University College has no men's residence," Tyndall said idly, as he tried to lead his irascible friend along the corridor.

"Wait a minute, Tyndall," the English professor said in a sharp challenging tone as he stopped and faced Tyndall. "Is that just a casual remark?"

"Why, no, of course not," Tyndall said uneasily. "I think it's apparent to everybody."

"Hm, is it?" the English professor said cynically. "I suppose it's apparent to rich men who have some money to leave to the University."

"Well, perhaps not."

"And I suppose it's apparent to politicians?" he said raising his voice.

"That's something else," Tyndall said, his uneasiness increasing.

"It's always something else," the English professor said belligerently. His eyes were bright and angry as he raised one fist like a man about to launch into a loud impassioned speech. "Now we're at the whole root of the matter," he began. "A world full of powerful but practical men who concentrate on what they believe to be useful things. And I know what I'm talking about, Tyndall."

"Of course you do. We go in here, don't we?" Tyndall said soothingly, as he pointed to the open door of the meeting-room.

"Wait a minute, Tyndall," the professor said impatiently. Grabbing Tyndall's arm he walked him past the open door. "I'm telling you that the practical men can always raise money. Research! Engineering!" the professor went on, talking loudly. "Of course, you can show a practical business man a laboratory. A little later on show him on his desk what comes out of the laboratory. My God, Tyndall!" the professor said vehemently. "What's the greatest laboratory of them all? A residence. What comes out of it? Human beings. Understand? Human beings, Tyndall."

At the open door of the classroom where the meeting was being held a head suddenly appeared. A gravely rebuking expression was on the earnest face. A finger was raised to the lips. "Sh, sh, sh, please," whispered the gentleman.

"He says, 'Sh, sh, sh,'" mocked the old professor. "Imagine. I live my life here. I try to express a little concern for the place and they say, 'sh, sh, sh.' Who is that fellow? Never saw him before in my life."

"A citizen. It's his meeting, I suppose," Tyndall whispered, growing more embarrassed. He wanted to steer his friend along the corridor away from the meeting before he humiliated himself. The gleam in the older man's eyes worried him; he had become difficult, inconsiderate and suddenly arrogant.

"Let's go somewhere where we can really talk," Tyndall whispered soothingly as he led him along the hall.

"I'm saying what I want to say, Tyndall. What's the matter, am I boring you?"

"No, no, no," Tyndall said quickly. "I'm more interested in what you have to say than in anything that will be said in the meeting. Let's go over to my place. Let's talk."

"As you say, Tyndall," he agreed. As he walked out with Tyndall he suddenly grew quiet. It may have been the cold winter air, or his surprise at finding someone who was encouraging him to talk, but he let himself be led along the path to Hart

House and up the stairs to Tyndall's quarters, where he took off his coat and accepted a cigar. But he remained strangely quiet, looking at the unlighted cigar and wondering why Tyndall had led him there. Then a hurt look came into his eyes. "Are you sure I wasn't making a nuisance of myself over there, Tyndall?" he asked.

"I didn't really want to go to that meeting," Tyndall said, shrugging. "We had got on to an interesting subject. Something I had thought a lot about myself."

"Is that a fact, Tyndall? You see I've bored everybody around here. I never talk about these things any more." He wanted to apologize for being what he was but the words wouldn't come easily. Frowning, he pondered, and the light shone on his bald head as he bit at the cigar. The fact that Tyndall was sitting beside him, at ease with him, moved him. It made the words more difficult. "I'm a teacher, Tyndall," he explained quietly. "I love being a teacher. I think I was born to work with students. Well, some years ago I began to feel I had practically no personal relationship with the students. The classes got bigger. It's a big college. It gets bigger every year, and they just come and go and get on street cars, and they never get close to me and I never get close to them. It's an empty life for a teacher, Tyndall."

"I hear it on all sides," Tyndall said gently, for he was strangely touched himself, perceiving now that this man must at one time have loved young students and wanted to share their life with them. What happened to them had been desperately important to him.

"Just what kind of a residence would you have in mind?" Tyndall asked, affecting a casual tone.

"Well, it wouldn't be simply a boarding-house," his friend answered cautiously, but he leaned closer to Tyndall; his fierce old eyes had softened. It's beautiful to have a man reveal the vision that has caused him unhappiness and made him a nuisance, and do it as if the vision were still fresh and new in his heart. "I can see it in my mind, Tyndall. I've been looking at it for twenty years. A building of simple architecture, true to the country. That would be important. I'd build it around a dining-room and a common-room. It's important to have men eat together. The breaking of bread together is an ancient rite. And the common-room is where men brush against each other and mould each other's lives. Do you follow me, Tyndall?" he asked.

It was not what he was saying that moved Tyndall but the sudden youthfulness that came over him as he saw himself living his life over again. His face was alive, his words had a ring to them. He saw himself as a young master with a student community growing around him, with the students coming to his room to carry on their problems that had only begun in the classroom. All were on the same social plane, all sharing the same accommodation and the same kind of life.

And there he was with his students, separated from the distractions of city life, from the swirl of alien influences that is always working against the discipline of the mind. And he would know the joy and excitement of sharing those intellectual dilemmas that often warp a student's life; he would be there as the helpful master. They would be all one in a community of spirit. "You know, Tyndall," he said, after a long pause in which he carried on his dream, "I believe in the undenominational college. I'm never troubled when they tell me that in my college we have no goal, no ideal. Of course, we don't subscribe to a theological pattern. But if we were living together we would be producing individuals as persons. The truth would be where we found it . . . We would have one goal, the stimulation of our mind by the quest for the truth. From there on we wouldn't have to worry. A student could go out into the world and create his own design."

From the open window came the sound of voices, a burst of loud laughter, the tramp of feet. The students had been holding the Assault-at-Arms, the inter-Faculty boxing and wrestling competition, in the big gym in Hart House, and now they were on their way home. In the stillness of the crisp cold air their voices carried across the campus. "I'm ashamed of you! In spite of the fact that I died laughing I'm ashamed of you," jeered one of them. "That little guy from S.P.S. hardly hit you, but your grandmother must have convinced you that you have a glass jaw." "I at least had some competition," answered the insulted one. "You don't fight. You just get on your bicycle." There was more snickering and laughing and the voices faded away.

"Well, I've taken up a lot of your time, Tyndall," said the professor with a sigh, for the laughter had broken his dream.

"No, no, no," Tyndall protested anxiously. In his own eyes now there was a far-away and wondering expression. The mathematician, having his little private joke, had assured him that this lonely old man had a passion. Well, he had. He wanted to give all of his life to the students of his college. Only that and nothing more. But the facilities weren't there; he had grown warped, irritable and a bore to more patient men. But for a teacher his passion was a noble one. He was a Balzacian character in quest of his absolute, and Balzac would have understood and loved him.

To ease him away gradually from his fixed idea Tyndall began to talk about the old days, of Bishop Strachan and Daniel Wilson and the controversies with Ryerson. They talked pleasantly for another hour and when Tyndall got the professor's coat for him he draped it gently around his shoulders.

They walked across Queen's Park, shook hands warmly. On the way back Tyndall's mind was still filled with those snatches of conversation about Strachan, Ryerson and Wilson. The old professor with his stories had made the past come alive for Tyndall.

Passing the bandstand, walking slowly and musing, while the moonlight shone on the shadowed strips of snow and on the naked trees with their snow-laden branches, it seemed suddenly to Tyndall that this place under the pallid light could easily belong to the dead. Tonight the ghosts of those old stalwarts could come flitting forth from their separate strongholds. He seemed to see the ghostly Bishop strolling down from Hoskin, stopping to eye the Memorial Tower with vast approval, for it was a bit of Anglican Oxford in a pattern dear to his heart. Suddenly he would realize that he was standing in the shadow of a building which was now U.C. but was to have been his College, and that his misty substance would pale out and he would become just a beam of moonlight if he loitered there; and he would shudder and duck past the college like a mother turning aside from a wayward child. There in the park he would wait sedately as ghostly bishops wait.

Drifting down the slope from Victoria would come the shade of Ryerson, knowing that the Bishop would be there first. The Bishop was always there first. In the snow under the moon they would stand well apart from each other, waiting for President Daniel Wilson. It was difficult to get Wilson out of the shadowy halls of U.C. for these sacred rites. He wasn't exactly an earth-bound, but rather a U.C.-bound ghost. But there he was now, taking his time, a slow-moving circle of light coming closer. And when he had stopped they would circle around each other with ectoplasmic grace, each awaiting his chance for an ironic thrust.

"I always hurry by your college, my dear Wilson," the Bishop would say sardonically.

"My college? Really, Strachan."

"Yes," the Bishop would go on, with vast spiritual superiority.

"I feel my substance paling every time I pass it. It's all so negative in there now since they gave up the ghost—I mean, of course, the Holy Ghost. Education directed towards no suitable moral goal."

While Ryerson hovered around like an indulgent chairman the wraith of Wilson would ponder and ask fairly, "And what end should we have had in mind, Strachan?"

"Wilson," the Bishop would answer tartly, "will it take you another fifty years in our nether world to realize man has an end?"

"Oh, I know that you, Bishop, always had a certain earthly sense of direction," Wilson would answer with the smile of a ghost. "But I don't mind what you call the negative aspects of my old college since you went your way. We seek the truth there for the truth's sake. I heard an old professor express it well enough tonight. A fine good man. I hear all these things. You know well, Strachan, that you and I, a couple of poor ghosts, can only try now to draw closer to the truth. It's our task now. But you tried to shape this University to your own pattern."

"And he failed," Ryerson would snap, "because he didn't grasp the economic and political power of my rising Methodist middle class. Really, Strachan, you ought to understand by this time that there's no family compact in heaven."

"I'm not sure of it," the Bishop would say slowly. "When you get closer to the light, Ryerson, you will understand perhaps that there is a hierarchy in heaven. By the way, your Victoria has gone a long way beyond you. I hear they look annoyed around there if one refers to the Puritan tradition. And haven't you heard that they'll be having a beauty contest at Victoria in a few years?"

"Gentlemen," Wilson would admonish them. "We're in this together. We have certain obligations. We have no choice. Let's get ahead with it."

"Just the same I always fail to understand why no one from t. Michael's is compelled to join us here," Ryerson would com- lain.

Putting out their ghostly hands and forming a little circle hey would begin their sedate and formal dance, circling around n the wan glimmer, gradually drawing a little closer until they ecame one grand ghostly pillar of light. And this pillar of light vould broaden and rise and soar into space and disappear, re- easing the old ghosts from their earth-bound follies.

Tyndall, smiling at this little conceit on his way through the ark, assured himself that those old ghosts would surely under- tand and love the English professor. The poor man wanted to ee a way of life at his college. But didn't that mean that he now ailed to see any design? If so, then he was like him, like Tyndall. t was very comforting. What disturbed him probably disturbed nany other men around there. And Tyndall began to whistle, or it was like seeing that he had company.

CHAPTER SIX

HE back campus, which is behind University College and off the west wing of Hart House, is the first place to catch the sunlight on the break-up of winter. The snow and ice on the level ground are like a target for the sun slanting over Whitney Hall. Soon there are pools of water, then patches of muddy earth. The ground dries in the sun. The first green grass appears. At noontime in the spring you can see the students walking gingerly across new green grass, testing its firmness and dryness, and soon, with the sunlight getting stronger, they began to play catch there. With the final exams not far off they stretch out on the grass in pairs, their books beside them, and the grass is now very green; and green, too, are the trees along Hoskin and down the path by the Cloisters. And along Hoskin, wearing their gowns, come the girls from St. Hilda's and the men from Trinity.

On that same campus in the autumn inter-Faculty teams play Mulock cup games. Sometimes there are two games going on at the same time. A line of spectators down the middle of the field watch first one game, then the other. The hoarse defiant yells of the Arts colleges, and Meds, and Engineers, have echoed for years across that campus. These inter-Faculty teams, especially in the beginning of the season, are rarely dressed smartly; the players wear odds and ends of football gear; and as the autumn wears on and a mist settles over the field and the ball soars over the line of the Hart House roof in the twilight, it is sometimes hard for a player to recognize his own men.

None of the students gathered there in the twilight would have believed that Arthur Tyndall often stood at a window watching them with a kind of furtive intensity. He was like a woman who carefully draws back a curtain and peers out at her neighbours. These students were accustomed to seeing the Warden hurrying briskly through the corridors of Hart House, or hearing him make quick suggestions at committee meetings, or watching him control unobtrusively the tremendous organization of the place. They all liked him. They had got used to his slightly alien accent. They liked the interest he took in any one of them who would bother to stop and talk to him. He seemed to them to be a big friendly easy-going man who wanted to draw close and make their personal lives important to him. They often agreed that he had a remarkable respect for their own way of doing things.

At night when he was alone in his own room he would be reading the poetry of Catullus. It would be quiet and peaceful, the room smelling beautifully of fine pipe tobacco, the smoke curling from his pipe. Then gradually there would steal into his mind the memory of the students passing him on the front campus on that day when he had decided that the University had no tone or atmosphere of its own. Frowning, he would put down his book and begin to think of all the fields of knowledge being cultivated around the campus so that men might live more wisely with each other, and he would try again to fit them into a scheme. Something was lacking, something without which there could be no harmonious pattern to shape a man's life. Or something was hidden. He would find himself putting these fields of knowledge together making a synthesis, then shaking his head impatiently. A harmony was lacking. He couldn't feel it, he couldn't hear it. The Research men were supposed to be impersonal, the Engineers were practical men. The Arts men were supposed to supply the tone. Why didn't they?

Then he would get up and take out his father's silver flute from its case and sit by the window and begin to play softly; then he would let the melody die away and sit there quietly for a long time.

In the lives of the students who came into Hart House he began to look for the elusive links in the pattern. He would pause and listen outside the music room. He would go downstairs to the billiard room and look in on the expert loafers under the cones of light over the green tables: and there with the click of the billiard balls in his ears he would observe the hearty healthy faces of the football players who always were able to get a billiard table and usually hung on to it. In little snatches of conversation about girls, or the whistling of a popular song, or in the way the students danced at a Hart House dance or acted in a play in the theatre or took direction from the director, he found some significant meaning. He stored it away in his head. He caught the intonation of their speech, the Ontario accent, the way they said "hoose" for "house" and "oot" for "out". They dressed casually but conservatively, without the outlandish flair for college clothes found in some American universities. No, they weren't quite American, they didn't have the breezy friendliness and the direct questioning of Americans—"Who are you, pal?"

"What do you do?" Nor were they politely retiring, like Englishmen. They didn't want to walk in the shadows. They liked being untroubled in their clear bright world. The dreamer, the tortured soul was rare among them.

When Tyndall expressed himself aloud in words he could be vague; he rambled on cheerfully, making friendly gestures and waving his pipe and trying severely the patience of sharper-minded men. He knew this. When he really wanted to think he used to sit down and organize his thoughts on paper. His written reports or opinions were exquisitely sharp and clear. He would sit late at night in his own room, smoking and making little notes in a black notebook.

He did not write so often now to Miss Phyllis Hallam in Wellington, New Zealand. The last time he wrote her he said, "I can't seem to make up my mind about this place. It has become for me now a nice intellectual problem and quite absorbing." So his light burned and he pondered over his notes and dreamed.

His light was not the only one in the neighbourhood that burned late at night. Lights burned in the windows of research laboratories. Other men also had been troubled by their dreams. Other men had tried stubbornly to create a little design from isolated bits of knowledge. Not far away, in the physiological department of the Medical building, in a makeshift laboratory, two young doctors had done some research work two years ago on the pancreas of dogs. One of these doctors said later that if he had known as much about the problem at the beginning of his quest as he did at the end he never would have started and therefore never would have succeeded. Tyndall had heard about the work Banting and Best had been doing, but it would never have occurred to him that Banting was a dreamer even as he himself had become a dreamer.

Banting had the idea that if cells producing pancreatic juice, a digestive fluid, could be made inactive, an extract of the pancreas might contain an active substance needed for the treatment of diabetes. And one morning Tyndall picked up a newspaper and read that Dr. Banting had been awarded the Nobel Prize. All over the world newspapermen were telling the story of the research work at the University of Toronto.

But Tyndall had no recollection of having ever met Banting and it troubled him. Was he something special, or were there other men capable of similar achievements coming into the Faculty room every day? Gossip trails in the wake of all great attainments. Around the University Tyndall heard little stories touched with malice. Learned men said, with that deprecating air that had bewildered Tyndall, "Of course the discovery of insulin was inevitable. If Banting and Best hadn't found the secret, somebody else would have."

One night at a party given by a publisher in Forest Hill, Tyndall met Banting. It was a dress affair for a visiting English novelist. In the dining-room fifty guests sat down for a late supper; and Banting in white tie and tails, sitting at the big table at the left of the plump novelist, turned out to be a big raw-boned man with a heavy stubborn face and a shy smile. He had a large firm nose, a long face, and none of the easy aplomb or the winning little social mannerisms that would have endeared him to a ladies' club. Tyndall, at a little table opposite Banting, watched him alertly. He seemed to be slow of speech, yet he had a kind of appealing warm sincerity.

After the supper when the guests broke up into little groups on the way to the drawing-room, Tyndall, edging his way closer to Banting, introduced himself, kept in step with him and made friendly small talk about the University. Both men were a little shy.

At the door of the drawing-room they were joined by a dark-haired young man in a dinner jacket, who was alone and ill at ease for he was the only one there wearing a black tie. He was a young writer who had just published his first novel. Breaking in on Tyndall he introduced himself with a shy hopefulness. "Why, of course," Banting said, greeting him warmly like an old friend. "Why, I remember reading the first story you ever published. Wait a minute. Let's sit down here on the stairs."

When Banting and the young writer sat down on the wide blue-carpeted stairs, Tyndall also sat down with them. By this time the other guests had all gone into the drawing-room.

"I liked that story of yours because it seemed to be about us, about you and me," Banting said to the young writer. "I mean, it was our landscape. The characters there against a background you could recognize." Looking around furtively, he slapped the young writer on the knee. "Let's go back there to the dining-room where we can talk," he whispered. He also offered an apologetic smile to Tyndall who accepted it as an invitation. The three of them, walking back to the dining-room, sat down in a corner where they could not be seen and where Banting and the young writer hoped they would be forgotten.

Tyndall was content to listen and watch as Banting began to talk about his fondness for reading. He talked about his own home and his boyhood. His liking for reading had been instilled in him by his father who used to read to the family group in their farmhouse. His father read aloud and read well, and the corners of the room were always in darkness, with just a circle of light around the big table. Banting was talking slowly, talking out of a genial memory, with a little smile on his face and a far-away look in his eyes. The ceiling light shone on one side of his face. It was not a particularly clever face, but it was earnest and good, and with the words he was using he was drawing the young writer close to him. They had quickly become like two old friends from the same neighbourhood who were opening up their lives to each other. As Tyndall studied Banting's face he was puzzled by a curious sense of recognition. It was as if he had seen it before, or had heard the voice and encountered the same kind of character many times.

"Well, you'll probably go to the States now that you've had a little success," Banting was saying. "But I hope you don't. You see, you and I, each in his own way, are really interested in the same thing. You want to be an artist with words. I want to go on with my research work." As the young fellow nodded and looked grateful, Banting, who had taken a pencil from his pocket, began to sketch on a paper napkin a cartoon of a citizen who was now in the drawing-room.

"I'd like to see us stay here where we belong," Banting said.

"Oh, quite," Tyndall agreed.

"Yes," Banting said, smiling vaguely at Tyndall. "What I want to do is find a way of keeping the creative people who come out of the University right here where they belong. Of course, it means the raising of a lot of money."

"Well, there seems to be a lot of money around," Tyndall said.

"Yes," Banting said, with the same vague smile at Tyndall. Drawing his chair closer to the young writer, he went on, "You're a writer. Well, tell me this then. How are we going to make this seem important to the imagination of the Canadian people?"

"Yes, that's the question," Tyndall said, trying hard to get into the conversation.

"What you're dealing with," said the young writer slowly, "is a failure of the imagination all around us. Maybe it's a failure to put any value on the imagination. It's the Canadian condition. Isn't that right?"

"I'd certainly say so," Tyndall agreed warmly. Sitting with a happy little smile on his face, he exuded a glow of vast satisfaction. He felt surprisingly elated. The buzz of voices came from the drawing-room, but the voices and room seemed to be a long way off. Tyndall knew that these two men weren't paying much attention to him, and that his occasional remarks were the remarks of one who didn't quite belong in the conversation. But he didn't mind. He believed that both Banting and the young fellow would like to be sitting with their coats off; in fact, they had withdrawn to the back room where they could be themselves. Tyndall was smiling to himself because he believed he had made a remarkable discovery. The University, and the whole country, had a vast back room where these people relaxed and were themselves. The visitor, the stranger, found these people to be one thing publicly; but if he could only get into the back room . . . And now, Tyndall was smiling and feeling elated because he had sneaked into the back room.

Looking up suddenly he saw the dark-haired opulent hostess standing at the door, a worried expression on her face. He joined her at once.

"Why don't you come into the drawing-room, Mr. Tyndall?" she asked.

"I've been in there with the boys," he said, taking her by the arm and leading her back to the hall.

"I beg your pardon?" she said, looking mystified. "Some people would like to meet Dr. Banting. He always seems to disappear. He does this at a lot of parties."

"He likes being with the boys in the back room. I do, too," Tyndall said, chuckling to himself as he led her away.

At noontime next day, a wet spring day, Tyndall was coming down the cinder path approaching the west entrance of the Parliament Building. He was having lunch with a provincial cabinet minister: he was always having lunch with someone in the high places. At noon hour the medical students come stream-

ıg up the paths from the General Hospital and turn into the
natomy building, or go on up the path towards Hart House.
tanding in the rain while groups of them passed him, Tyndall
ound himself looking into their faces and asking himself why
ıese boys had begun to impress him even before his first en-
ounter with Banting. What was it that gave so many of them a
quality, a dignity that you had to respect? It was hard to define;
fter all, like the rest of the student body, they came from all
ver Ontario and from the West. Was it because they were care-
ully screened on admittance and had to work hard? If that were
o, he reflected, you could expect them to be a pretty solemn
rowd, but the fact was that their theatrical evening, "Daffydill",
vas the most exuberantly rowdy of all the college performances.
Jo, it was more likely because they were always dealing with
uman material. And how was it that they could develop a
radition of their own which was curiously liberal and which
ermitted them to believe in public service? It must have been
ecause they had some fine Deans and some remarkable teachers:
hey could take pride in the great creative surgery of a Gallie,
or the technical perfection of a Roscoe Graham, and in the fact
hat some of the textbooks written by their teachers were used
ıll over the world.

As they passed in the rain and he kept looking at them,
Tyndall suddenly smiled, for he knew now why Banting had
ooked familiar to him last night. It was true that he had seen
ıim before. Banting had been the familiar Ontario boy. In him
ast night he had caught a glimpse of a thousand Ontario boys
rom little towns who had come to the University of Toronto.
Maybe they would never have the peculiar dogged persistence,
or the kind of brain that made Banting what he was, but they
elonged to the same pattern; they came off the same wide
streets in the Ontario towns; they knew the gabled farmhouses

and the silence of the long winters; they loafed together in the hot summer sunlight. Incapable of operatic gestures they were a little diffident, liking the stag parties, the fishing parties, seeking in their companions the earthy kind of friendship, but believing always in the good job honestly and cleanly done.

"Hello there, Mr. Tyndall," called a stocky student, hatless and wearing a trench coat, who was coming down the cinder path.

"Hello there," Tyndall answered, waving a greeting.

He had met this medical student last year when the student had been taking an Arts course. This year he had switched to Meds, and had told Tyndall why he had done so. Last summer he had worked on the lake boats, and in some small port had got hold of a copy of Sir William Osler's lectures for medical students. On his ship he had read these lectures again and again, and his mind and his heart had been stirred and he had come rushing back to college to change the whole plan of his life and study medicine.

As Tyndall turned away and went on up to the drive to the Parliament Buildings he remembered these facts about the boy in the trench coat walking hatless in the rain. Suddenly he stopped, for what he remembered of the student seemed to have a remarkable importance. It had to do with his own intellectual problem and its solution. It was as though Tyndall had heard one of those strange interior voices that a man in his bed at night sometimes hears, saying, "There it is. Right in there some- where. It's what you've been after." But the illumination was so fleeting and fugitive it slipped right away from him and he missed it. Turning in the rain he watched the student go down the path, and his own thoughts gathered in a kind of stupid knot. He shook his head, wondering what he had missed, and then went on in to meet his cabinet minister.

CHAPTER SEVEN

F THE President had been aware that Tyndall had the thoughts and feelings of a stranger, keeping him apart from the life around him, he could reasonably have insisted that Tyndall was no man for his job. But they were all unaware of his alien moods. Like a certain celebrated Frenchman, Tyndall knew that it was easier to conform and he functioned so expertly in his role at Hart House that everyone continued to speak of him with approving smiles. And, of course, he didn't go back to New Zealand that summer. He accepted an invitation to go on a fishing trip in Northern Ontario, and then one of the Board of Governors invited him to spend a month in the Laurentians. There was some correspondence with Miss Hallam, who had expected him to come home. Tyndall felt ashamed of himself as he tried to explain to her his peculiar interest in the University. He was ashamed, too, of being unable to make a clean break with Toronto and of going back there in the fall with such an eager unsatisfied curiosity.

85

He became particularly friendly with Tom Lane, a day scholar at Trinity. Lane was a heavy-shouldered, long-legged fellow with thick black hair and dark defiant eyes, the son of a Toronto druggist. As a scholar it was inevitable that he be despised, because he had elected to take the Pass Arts Course. No one in authority has much use for a man or a woman who takes such an easy course. The honour students assume that the pass course student plans to be a loafer or a gentleman, or that his father does not know what to do with him. It is also assumed that a Pass Arts girl is continuing a course begun at some finishing school. A mild and gentle professor of history was once heard to declare vehemently in the Faculty room that he would take all the pass course students and dump them into an enlarged high school beyond the city limits; they are the ones who go in for horseplay, he said; they are the ones who loaf and idle and drag down the intellectual tone of the whole University. In a fit of remorse he added mildly that some day they should all do something for these students who have become the intellectually underprivileged.

Not only was this big alert fellow, Tom Lane, in the pass course, but he had selected a list of subjects that bewildered the Registrar of his own college. "You're planning to take French, English, a little philosophy and some economics, Lane," said the Registrar. "But I see you also plan to take mineralogy. You know, don't you, it means that in the second year you'll be taking palaeontology and then geology? What in the world are you taking those subjects for, Lane?"

"I've got friends who are science men, sir," Lane said soberly. "I'm always hearing of the scientific method. Maybe I'll get interested in it."

"But as a pass student, you should at least try and stress the humanities, shouldn't you, Lane?"

"Oh, I expect to do that all my life anyway, sir," Lane said with a shrug. "And a little of this other stuff may get into my way of thinking."

"Hm," began the Registrar dryly, "and you imagine that if you sit around in the sunlight . . ."

"I may get a little sunburnt. That's it, sir," Lane said seriously.

As a student at Trinity in the time of Provost Seager, Lane simply sat around in the sunlight.

Old Bishop Strachan, when he founded Trinity, had written, "We desire a university which, fed by the heavenly stream of pure religion, may communicate fuel to the lamp of genius and enable it to burn with a brighter and purer flame." Lane was not aware of these words of the founder of his college and so sometimes he was in the heavenly stream and sometimes he wasn't. The Anglican customs of his college he accepted with an innocent pleasure. He didn't want to miss anything. When an upper classman asked who he was, he was expected to reply "Worm Lane, sir". He was even worse than an ordinary "worm". He was also known as a "rabbit" because he came to the college from his hole in the city. Most of the students in the Trinity residence, which in those days was the big old apartment hotel at the corner of St. George and Harbord, had come from the prep. schools. They represented a certain economic independence; they had known each other at Ridley or U.T.S. or Upper Canada, so Lane was at a disadvantage. The only trouble was that he never realized he was at a disadvantage. The black tie of mourning which freshmen are supposed to wear he discarded after the first two days, and since he was powerful and self-reliant nobody did much about it; and besides, some professor was always there to deplore the horseplay of initiations. But at Sunday morning chapel he appeared in his gown. The girls from St. Hilda's, the "saints", were also there in their mortar-boards and gowns. Being a day scholar

Lane would too frequently hear Dr. Kingston saying to him patiently, "If you can't get there in the morning why can't you get there at six o'clock?"

Lane met Tyndall the night of the first Hart House debate, but even before they spoke to each other and shook hands they had been sharing the same delightful sense of discovery without knowing it.

That opening debate was a full-dress affair in the big hall on the second floor which had been used until then as a common- and reading-room. The speaker's dais had been erected against the wall between the wide windows, and the floor of the house was divided: you sat either to the left or to the right of the speaker. The first Labour government had recently been elected in England. That night in Hart House they were debating a resolution expressing confidence in the Labour government. Invitations had been sent out to many eminent figures around town, and when they came and soberly took their places to the right or the left that hall suddenly became not just a student forum, but a place for the expression of influential Toronto opinion. The speaker of the House was Professor Gilbert Jackson, the economist, in white tie and tails. The government forces were led by the white-haired Professor John McNaughton, and a St. Michael's student; the opposition by that energetic and challenging economist C. R. Fay, and a student from S.P.S.

Tyndall, of course, as a lover of established tradition, was sitting with the opposition. But young Lane, a freshman, believing that he ought to belong to the future, sat with the Labour supporters.

The arrangement was familiar to Tyndall because he had been at Oxford and the procedure followed was that of the Oxford Union. He liked these debates. But he couldn't help wondering how these Toronto students would conduct themselves. To Lane, however, it was all unfamiliar but he, too, was waiting to see how it would work out and whether he would be able to comport himself happily and with distinction.

In the first few dull formal moments it was as if they were all getting used to being there with each other. Soon a kind of excitement came over everybody. It may have been that the question before the house was controversial and easily inflamed the imagination of the speakers and their followers, or that the lights gleaming on the stiff white shirts and the beards and the bald heads of the visitors dazzled the students and set them free and made them eager for grandeur. From the beginning there was an impetuosity, a recklessness, a laughing challenge in the speeches. Yet the rules of the house were accepted willingly. Low-hanging ceiling lights glowed on rows of serious alert faces. The St. Mike's man, speaking vehemently, was having trouble with his boiled shirt which kept billowing out from the black vest. He kept pounding it in with his fist as he talked. The Speaker, listening with a gravely intense concentration, silenced interruptions. Then, for Tyndall, the whole hall unexpectedly took on a sudden glow. Touched by the happy eagerness of the occasion he looked around in wonder and he made a little discovery. A sense of freedom and independence had been so natural to these Canadian students that they had never bothered to assert their rights passionately, and until now he had never realized that this sense of freedom was simply a part of their natural equipment. If it was there it might be hard for anyone to curb it. It might be that the very structure of the University engendered and protected it. In a state University freedom in education and discussion might be at the whim of a group of politicians, but here at Toronto the autonomous Arts colleges, those with their various religious faiths, would always assert this freedom for the protection of their own teaching and their faiths.

The peculiar structure of the federation was a barrier against the political power. It was a comforting thought. It was remarkable that Tyndall hadn't perceived it before. This kind of free debate belonged in that pattern of freedom. It was exciting. His eyes began to shine, he folded his arms across his chest, he sat back with a pleased smile; for this hall was in his domain. He seemed to see the years opening up and this free forum for free students established as part of the tradition of university life, achieving such renown that all men of passion and conviction from far parts of the country, cabinet ministers, economists, prime ministers, defenders of the most unorthodox ideas, and brave tilters at windmills, would answer an invitation eagerly and feel at home here with a gay sense of freedom.

And Tom Lane, sitting well back in the hall, was also making a happy discovery; but for him it was more like the discovery of a place that he had known to exist, for it had already existed in his imagination. He could see himself making a hundred eloquent speeches in this hall; all he wanted was a chance to speak at this moment. When he finally got the eye of the Speaker he made an extemporaneous, slightly impudent speech dealing with the remarks of those who had spoken ahead of him. It was then that Tyndall noticed Lane. Most of the students had made carefully rehearsed speeches. But the big dark fellow, a freshman, spoke spontaneously and freely out of his own heart in an easy natural tone and with flashes of wit; and Tyndall, smiling broadly, liked him.

When the debate was over, Tyndall, going along the crowded corridor, saw the big fellow and stopped. "That was a pretty good speech," he called. "I don't think I remember your name."

"The name is Lane, Tom Lane. And thanks, sir," Lane said, grinning with embarrassment.

"Well, let's shake hands," Tyndall said.

"I'd be glad to," Lane said and he shook hands and suddenly felt at ease with Tyndall and liked him.

Tyndall didn't see much more of Lane until the following year when Lane, a sophomore now, became a member of the Hall Committee. One day after a committee meeting Tyndall had sat around talking with three of the students, one of them Lane; another, a tall serious S.P.S. student, Joe Gibbons; and the third one a philosophy student from St. Mike's, W. J. O'Rourke.

"I see you around Hart House a lot now, Lane, don't I?" Tyndall asked.

"I hang around a lot," Lane agreed. "I'm a day scholar."

"Why shouldn't he hang around?" the S.P.S. student said cynically. "He's got nothing else to do. It's that gentlemanly course of his."

"It's a fact," agreed O'Rourke. "Four years of beautiful bumming. He's taking the 'once-over-lightly' treatment from the intellectual barber."

"I know you're an engineer," Lane said with a grin to the student from S.P.S. "I know you haven't any time to get an education."

"I have lectures and lab work that take thirty-six hours a week," the S.P.S. student said, nettled a little. "I can't sit around like you can in that library upstairs and fall asleep and then wake up and go on reading the novel that put me to sleep."

"As I say," Lane repeated. "One of these days you may get time to read a book."

"There's nothing I'd like better," the S.P.S. student said with dignity. "I like to read as much as you do, but if I do it it's on borrowed time. I'd like to be a gentleman too, if my professors could only be persuaded that I didn't have to pass any exams."

"It's a thing Lane wouldn't understand," said the philosophy student, O'Rourke. "Don't go into it too deeply. Lane in his course doesn't have to go into anything deeply. He may end up as a gentleman but certainly no scholar."

"All right," Lane said cheerfully, and Tyndall noticed he wasn't embarrassed at all. "You're over there at St. Mike's going into your philosophy deeply. Maybe you'll end up knowing exactly what St. Thomas or St. Augustine thought about the world, and I won't know it as well. Maybe you'll master their thought. But if any simple-minded student ever asks you a question about history or literature you'll look surprised and say, 'It wasn't my subject.' You're a pair of specialists. I have nothing to use but my own head."

"Without being trained in anything in particular," the S.P.S. student said sharply.

"Sure, just a poor pass student," Lane agreed. "Trying to get along in exalted company."

Lane was supposed to be the idle drifter, Tyndall knew. But he was self-assured and well informed. In his own way he was happy at the University. He might have his own perceptions; he might even be getting at the University the kind of general education professors talk about at dinners for visiting educators, but do not really believe in because of the drive for specialization. Leaving the committee room Tyndall linked his arm under Lane's and walked along the hall with him.

"If you're not doing anything, Lane, why not come up to my quarters and sit down for a while?" he said, leading him along carefully by the arm.

"Oh, I'm never doing anything, Mr. Tyndall," Lane said awkwardly.

"I don't believe you're loafing along so lazily," Tyndall said. When they were sitting down in his sitting-room and he had made Lane feel at home by offering him a cigarette, he went on,

"Or rather I should say that I don't think you're as lazy-minded as you pretend. But why don't you change over to an honour course?"

"Maybe I'm not cut out for really earnest scholarship, Mr. Tyndall."

"But real scholarship, Lane, would give your mind such a splendid training. Nothing is lovelier than a trained mind."

"I know it, sir," Lane agreed. When he felt he had to watch what he said he stuttered a little; it was only when he was frank that he was free and eloquent. "Sometimes I get an uneasy feeling about scholars, Mr. Tyndall," he tried to explain. "They seem to get tired. I mean a man should sometimes look around, see things freshly. I mean with his own eyes. I don't want to get trained to see the world through somebody else's eyes. I mean, sir," he blurted out, "I don't want to be just a ghoul."

"A ghoul?"

"Yes, sir. Living only in the minds of dead men."

"Oh, I see what you mean, Lane," the Warden said, chuckling a little and liking his impulsiveness. "Of course, some scholars are ghouls, but a lot depends on the man, doesn't it?"

"I know some men who are first-class honour students," Lane went on. "But so many of them have no time, sir. No free time. It's the free time. It's what happens to you in the free time when you're relaxed that really sticks in your mind and shapes your life, isn't it, Mr. Tyndall?" Then he looked embarrassed. "I guess I'm just born to be idle," he explained apologetically as he stood up.

"Yet I don't think you are idle, Lane," the Warden insisted. He wanted to keep him there talking. It was late in the afternoon. The last of the sunlight fell like a slanting pillar between them. It seemed to Tyndall that Lane did not belong in the regular mould of Toronto student life. He had his own strength and his own judgments. At Trinity or on the campus or in the university lecture rooms, Lane might appear to be beautifully at home, but Tyndall was convinced that he stood alone, that he had a flair for rebellion, that he had pitted himself against all the prevailing opinions and in spirit was really alien. In the heart Lane was as much a stranger as Tyndall was, and he was moved and felt himself drawn warmly to Lane. "What you think of as idleness, Lane, may be what the Greeks thought of as leisure. Their leisure was their university. We can have some fine talks about this, Lane. We'll see each other often."

Those idle hours were truly the source of much of Tom Lane's happiness. He had found that if he relaxed for a few moments he would start wondering about his own life and the lives of others. He was not afraid to be idle and alone. When he became an old man, no longer having the energy to be industrious, he would not be one of those who sit around regretting that they did not die in harness.

Lane's idle hours began in the early afternoon. He would come into the Hart House reading-room, to the left of the main entrance, sometimes as early as half-past two. His lectures finished, he would feel splendidly free. For half an hour he would loaf around from table to table picking up magazines and reviews, thumbing his way through them and sometimes sitting down with his leg curled over the arm of a chair to read an article. There within his reach were the great liberal weeklies from London and New York, *The New Statesman, The New Republic* and *The Nation.* Then he would go upstairs to the library and loaf around as if he were getting familiar with the layout of the place. He never seemed to be looking for anything in particular. On one of the shelves he would recognize the name of a writer who had been mentioned in a review he had been reading downstairs. In those days Shaw, Chesterton, Wells, and Mencken were the brilliant controversialists. These writers were always opening up a wider world for Tom Lane. He would wander from shelf to shelf becoming familiar with modern writers who weren't mentioned in his classroom, then he would look up at the clock and realize his Mulock Cup team was having a practice. Being a big fellow he was a pretty good middle wing. On the way out he would still be carrying on an argument with one of the great controversialists and coming to his own conclusions. Sometimes he used to feel a little guilty wandering into the Hart House library, for he would be skipping a lecture by persuading himself he was too late for it. He was convinced he was loafing because he felt wonderfully at ease and because he didn't have to pass examinations and no professor could say he was wrong. There in the quiet library, with the sunlight glinting on the red sofa and the natural weathered panelling, all was bathed in a soft glow, and it became a world in which he experienced a strange elation; he would feel capable of sharing in the bewildering creative vision of a great writer. He felt confident and even arrogant. It was as if those who had planned the library had said, "Put these books here, and they will be found unerringly by those to whom they can mean something." Curled up in one of the deep red couches Tom Lane would read Flaubert's *Madame Bovary* and the tragic ending would become like a shattering personal death. Years later, whenever he heard Flaubert's name mentioned, a picture of Hart House library—the red couch, the leaded windows, the carpet, the sunlight—would flash in his mind. He would stand at the window looking out at the sidewalk curving around U.C., watching the students in their coming and going, and dream of the great Flaubert. And the little phrase, "le mot juste", had such a powerful meaning for him that sometimes he would find himself repeating it to himself in the classroom. In those leisurely hours nothing was expected of him. It

95

was only a happy adventure, and sharing the adventure with him were those writers he seemed to pick only at random. Actually, of course, nothing was coming at random. If he were reading George Moore's *Confessions of a Young Man*, then Moore became his companion, and if Moore celebrated Balzac's greatness then Lane wanted to celebrate it too. Sometimes his heart would leap, he would want to sing; he was in a continual state of elation. On the shelves near the door there were some Russian novels; he was attracted by the strange name Dostoievsky on one of them. It was a story called *The Gambler*. Tom Lane had never heard of Dostoievsky but as he read this story the feverish excitement of the writer gripped him. For a month he became a Russian. Each week he discovered some magical name which seemed to open a window of his imagination, a window that he hadn't known existed.

If he fell asleep in the library (and the S.P.S. student was right in suggesting that he did), it was because he had been out late the night before, dancing: he had time to dance, he had time to debate, he had time to play footy-footy with the girls from St Hilda's in the Trinity library.

What was happening to Lane's mind in those idle hours did not make him a success in the lecture room. In an English class he could be irritating, arrogant, then sullenly contemptuous. A teacher often wished that Lane would concentrate more on the work in hand. Once in a philosophy lecture which he, being a Trinity student, took in the main building, he made a remark about Plato, and that tall sharp-witted professor who was Tyndall's friend, tripped him up neatly; he made a fool out of him. After the lecture Lane went down to the university library and got Plato's *Republic*; a week later he got the *Dialogues*. He lived with Plato for a month because he didn't want to sound like a fool again. Yet sometimes his seriousness would get mixed up with exuberance and he would feel like another kind of a fool.

One night in the winter after a lively debate in the Trinity Student's Parliament, Lane was on his way home. It came to him with a touch of amusement that most Trinity men liked to think of themselves as talkers: they saw themselves later on assuming responsible positions in the world where they would be required to talk a lot. He had come along Hoskin and was cutting through Queen's park on his way to Bay Street to get the street car. That night he believed he had made a pretty good speech, and as he strode along he could still hear the voices of his critics, only now he answered with a devastating power; he remembered a dozen apt quotations from the masters of literature; his mind leaped toward those observations that Shaw or Chesterton, Mencken or Balzac might have made; he seemed to be imbued with all the fiery wit and wisdom of the ages. Words tumbled out of him. In his sublime assurance all his thoughts raced; everything was clear. Suddenly he stopped and looked around at the moonlight shining on the snow. The bare trees made a lacy pattern of shadows on the whiteness. The college buildings rose around him. He knew he was experiencing a kind of elation he might never know again. He looked around with a yearning to draw everything close to him, the cold trees, the circle of lights, the fading towers of Hart House, the chimneys and snow-covered roof of his own unlighted college, and even the bandstand there in the park, which he passed so often. It all had at that moment a special significance; it was a part of this ascendancy of the mind giving him a free unlimited joy that he wanted to keep in his heart wherever he went. Then he laughed. He was laughing at himself. "I'm feeling like a fool," he thought.

In those days Tyndall was Lane's admirer, although, of course, Lane didn't know it. He only knew that their friendship

was developing and they shared fine moments of easy under-
standing. Tyndall used to talk to his friend, the old mathematician, about Lane. It was interesting, he said, to find a student
making good use of the pass course. But the mathematician was
adamant. "Your young friend Lane," he explained with that
dreadful precise finality that always ended an argument, "may
seem like a bright boy to you, Tyndall, because he has a ready
smattering of surface facts. But look a little deeper and you'll
find it's all unorganized."

"But when he's interested he always gets the facts."

"It is possible, Tyndall, that Lane may have found the one
right course suitable for his temperament. But even if he has
done so, take my word for it he'll be the only intellectual that
has emerged from the pass course in the last ten years." The
mathematician was smiling. His tone was gentle and persuasive.
He was always mild and amused when talking to Tyndall. "And if
your young friend, whom I have not had the pleasure of knowing
as you do, Tyndall, is able to make something of his idleness it
only points up a weakness in the honour courses. We should do
something to see that the honour students are given more leisure.
It is still the honour students who make a university. Otherwise,
scholarship and the trained mind amounts to nothing."

"Just the same I think Plato would have loved Lane," Tyndall
said stubbornly.

"Really. Why?"

"Because he's young and he rushes eagerly at ideas."

"Why pick on Plato, Tyndall?"

"It's a habit I got into around here," Tyndall explained with
a dry smile. "At Toronto everybody picks on Plato."

Across the road from the Trinity residence at the corner of
Harbord and St. George, was a little restaurant called the Old
Elm. It was run by a plump balding amiable man who was fond

of the horses. In this restaurant Lane was a great man. Here he would sit from three o'clock in the afternoon until midnight. Some of the brightest people around the University in those days used this little restaurant as their meeting house. It was a centre of intellectual fashion. Of course, it really wasn't much of a place, any more than a cellar on the left bank of the Seine or a flat in Greenwich Village would look much of a place to a visitor who didn't share the life that was led there. But here Tom Lane would sit gulping vast quantities of coffee, quoting T. S. Eliot, passionately defending Sinclair Lewis, dreaming of a success like Scott Fitzgerald's, and wondering if he was a member of the lost generation. The girls were bright. The men were angry. Sometimes they all hated each other. Sometimes, all together, they went down to Angelina's at midnight. They all believed they were of the small company who knew what was going on in the world. It was the last of the prohibition days, the end of the jazz age.

Tyndall would come to this restaurant to have a cup of coffee with Lane. Such little meetings had become important to Tyndall. He would join in the literary arguments, but his smile was apologetic for he read the *Saturday Evening Post* and John Galsworthy; and Lane, who had discovered new writers appearing in little magazines in Paris and New York, would make him feel like an old duffer. But he would earnestly write down the names of these new writers in a little black notebook. He would talk, listen, argue, laugh and feel wonderfully alive. He was enjoying for the first time the peculiar delight an older man gets in the company of a young fellow who is intelligent and has some perceptions of his own. He would feel a warm little glow and have a new belief in the possibilities of the human race.

And sometimes he would reveal to Lane his doubt about that impersonal way of life so many of them followed around the

University. "When you leave here, Tom," he said, "I wonder how many of your old professors you'll want to come back and see."

"Right now it would be hard for me to say, Mr. Tyndall."

"But will you look back and think of them as exciting men?"

"Well, let me see now. I'd have to get away first."

"But are there many? And if there are not, well, why? I often wonder. Doesn't it seem to you that something is lacking in the pattern around here, Tom?"

"I'm inside the pattern," Tom said. "How can I look at it?"

"That's right," Tyndall agreed. "But something is lacking. Some part of the pattern is never asserted," Tyndall went on stubbornly. "I'm still not quite sure what it is." And Lane felt uneasy because his friend seemed to be lonely and discontented.

CHAPTER EIGHT

HAT dark girl with the round face and the eager brown eyes, Helen Winston, from Regina, had met Tom Lane one night after a Trinity-Victoria debate, when he walked her back to her residence. It is a short pleasant walk along Hoskin to the crescent, even in the winter; and they made it a little longer by turning into the park and going down the path as far as the bandstand. It was a mild winter night. It had snowed and then thawed and the trees in the park were ice-coated and shimmering in the moonlight; and to the south the stone walls of the Parliament Buildings glistened, and the soft snow on the park was all white and new. The stars were shining, and Tom Lane had suddenly started quoting Keats' sonnet, "Bright Star, would I were steadfast as thou art". He had finished the whole sonnet, and she had assumed that he was taking honour English. When he told her he was only in the pass course she was startled and disappointed. But when he walked her home she said earnestly that she hoped he would phone her some night.

Now that she was in her third year she knew some of the splendour and desperation of being a pretty, intelligent girl, always standing high in her honour course, yet not being one of those "golden girls" who go to all the dances and have such an easy course that they never have to do any laborious work. The "golden girls" can be seen any afternoon in the bright fall sunlight, stretched on the grass on the back campus, or, in early spring, sitting in rows with their admirers on the steps of University College, or on the grass at the west wing of Burwash Hall. Nancy Willson, Helen's first room-mate, had been such a girl, but she had failed in her second year, and when her father in Brantford had suffered severe financial reverses, she had had to leave college. Nancy had wept and had talked about training for a nurse but the hospital discipline had been too painful for her and now she was working as a stenographer in Brantford.

Being quick-minded and sensitive, Helen sometimes wondered whether being a university woman would make her life more difficult. She knew now that she couldn't marry a man who was her intellectual inferior. Sometimes in her own classes, or in the walk past Hart House along by University College, she would find herself looking into the faces of the men and wondering which were the bright ones who would interest her. If none of them glanced at her she would feel a little tremor like the onset of a familiar loneliness. It was the loneliness she used to feel when hearing the phone ring hour after hour with another girl always being called to answer it. She knew also what it was like to go to a dance with someone who couldn't fill her card with the names of friends because he didn't have the right kind of dancing friends. She had sat and watched and listened while Annesley girls sat around in their rooms with their shoes off after the dance, their dresses discarded, in a cozy intimacy as they profoundly discussed the limitations of their escorts and took them to pieces and put them together again and discarded some of them forever.

One afternoon after a Varsity-McGill game Tom Lane had taken her to a fraternity dance on St. George Street, and in her heart she became much more than a golden girl; she felt she was important to a man who was vibrant and alert, an intelligent debater, whose mind seemed so alive because his knowledge was not organized as hers was. She felt she had a secret from the other girls; she felt she had found someone who made everything she had learned, every line she had read, every quick bright thought of hers, suddenly more important. She believed there was a splendid and sympathetic balancing of her mind with his. Not that she thought she was in love. It was only that she felt a new kind of ache when the phone rang, a new kind of expectancy, and a desolation when it rang all the time and no one called her to it. Then Lane would call again and she would know that delightful expectancy, wondering whether he would have the money to buy her a corsage. She would rush around in a glow, borrowing a dress, borrowing face creams, borrowing jewellery.

When he took her to the Hart House masquerade they didn't even have to take a taxi. She, dressed as a medieval maiden in crimson velvet and he as a big hulking clown, they walked down Avenue Road and along the crescent.

It was a fine masquerade, with the dancing in the great panelled hall. They promenaded slowly through the long stone corridors, and she felt truly that she was a medieval lady walking in cloistered halls that were forbidden to her and other women. They went upstairs to sit on the smooth stone bannister. In the half shadows, with Tom's arm coming around her, she watched and listened for footsteps echoing on the stone floor as he kissed her. Looking up quickly they were deeply embarrassed for there was a priest from St. Michael's college smiling to himself and pretending he hadn't seen them. Then the Gershwin melody came floating up from the hall, a fantastic music haunting a gray-shadowed monastic cloister, and the sense of being where she was forbidden to be delighted her.

Drawing away from him she said, "I don't know why you always refuse to tell me what you're going to do when you graduate, Tom."

"I'm not sure. That's all, Helen."

"You deliberately won't say, Tom. You tease me. What can you do with your course?"

"Nothing, unless I go on to law or medicine," he said, laughing.

"I've never been able to figure you out," she complained. "Why do you make me feel like a little grind?"

"You're kidding me," he chuckled. Gathering her suddenly in his big arms he put her on the wide stone bannister and sat behind her, and they slid all the way down the bannister, and there was Mr. Tyndall, who was merely looking around, smiling and bowing to them.

"You know something about your friend Mr. Tyndall?" Helen said. "He doesn't look as happy as he did the first time I saw him."

"No, I don't think he is particularly happy around here," Tom said, looking worried. "He's a wonderful guy but he seems to be lonely."

"What's the matter with him?"

"I guess a man has a right to make himself lonely in his own way," Tom said. "I don't think he can make up his mind about this place. A man either sees life clearly and sees it whole or he doesn't. I think he goes around here saying something is lacking, something is lacking. Even a crossword puzzle can drive you crazy if you let it keep you awake at nights."

"Supposing he found out what was lacking."

"I've got a hunch he'd go home. Right home."

"But what could be lacking? I feel so happy tonight, nothing seems to be lacking, Tom. Nothing in the world, and, oh, nothing around here."

"It's this intellectual problem. It's the relationship of the Faculties, the fields of knowledge to the men themselves. It's complicated," Tom said profoundly. "It's like trying to add it all up so you can say, Oh, yes, Toronto. That's dear old Toronto."

"It's like trying to justify the ways of God to men," she said laughing. It did not seem really important to either of them. "Come on, let's dance," she said.

On that slow beautiful dreamy walk back to her residence, with her crimson medieval gown trailing on the slushy sidewalk, and with Tom beside her, his fingers linked in hers, it became a night that could not end. "Why don't you break out of that hen roost occasionally?" he asked suddenly. "Why don't you join the Varsity staff? I'll put in a plug for you, Helen."

"It would be wonderful," she said. "I don't know why I never went after such a job. I'm so busy around my own college I never seem to have any time. Why do I feel right now I have all the time in the world? Or maybe such a little bit of time left." She got all confused. She was glad that it was dark and he could not see the blood suffusing her cheeks. Laughing nervously she said, "I guess I mean that at my back I always hear time's wingèd chariot hurrying near."

She did not admit to herself that she joined the Varsity staff believing that she would often be in Tom Lane's company. Those nights when she was down at the Varsity office, which was in the University of Toronto Press building, suddenly became like the filling-out of her college life. It was what she had wanted without knowing it. In that small office late at night—for when she worked at night she was permitted late leave—they all sat around on the tables like professional newspaper people who have just put their paper to bed. Some of them wore green eyeshades. The men were always in their shirt-sleeves. Citizens who were liberated from the confines of their own colleges, they wrote for their own amusement mocking editorials which were never printed, they wrote snatches of poetry. They were profoundly critical of each other's work; they dreamed of pieces that would startle the President and Board of Governors; they talked bravely of liberty of expression; but Helen's happiness came in being there late at night with them, sitting around and feeling that she had become a woman of the cosmopolitan world, a little beyond the reach of those girls in her own residence. This stirring enlargement of her life she felt most strongly when Lane walked her back to Annesley Hall.

Until the spring of her final year she enjoyed this simple, uncomplicated, secure happiness. The spring of a final year is a terrible time. When the snow melts on the campus and in the park, and the green grass appears and the girls in their bright dresses sit around on the steps, with the passing men eyeing them tenderly, when the nights become mild and caressing, a terrible restlessness comes into the heart of a girl like Helen Winston. This restlessness is bitterly frustrating because the spring-time is the time of anxiety and pressure, the time of the most exacting work. The hours when she would have liked to be walking with Tom Lane were the hours when she had to sit in her room at Annesley with the window open and the night birds calling and the cars purring softly down Avenue Road. She would sit at the desk in her room concentrating on her books, blotting out from her mind all the distracting dreams until there remained only the books there on the desk. Her parents expected her to graduate brilliantly and her self-respect demanded it too.

But one spring night she took a few hours off and walked with Tom Lane down that shadowed path by the cloisters of University College and on down by Simcoe and Convocation Halls. Even when the moon is bright that walk is dim and secluded. They had come thinking they would be exuberantly affectionate; instead, after the first few minutes they became grave; their conversation was strangely sedate; they walked slowly in step. "Knew from the first you had a fine mind, Helen," he said.

"Oh, no, you have the fine mind, Tom."

"No, you worked. Yours is a good mind, Helen, I'm a perverse kind of a student. I can't help it. Do you know that line of Emily Dickinson's about some scholar—'He has the facts but not the phosphorescence of learning'?"

"I never read Emily Dickinson, Tom."

"Well, I liked that line . . . the phosphorescence of learning— yes," he repeated with satisfaction. Then he asked solemnly, "What are you going to do now you're through around here?"

"I don't know, Tom."

"Will you teach?"

"Maybe. Oh, I don't know, Tom. I would like to do something with my education. It should help me to earn my living, shouldn't it?"

"Now, there you go! It's supposed to do something to you, Helen. But it sounds as if you'll stay on here where you are happy and do M.A. work, isn't that it, Helen?"

"What are you going to do, Tom?"

"Me? I don't know. I'd like to work my way to South America for a trip. You know, the old chase for beauty and adventure."

"Tom, tell me something, will you?"

"Why, sure."

"Why did you never take me out on Saturday nights?"

"Saturday nights," he repeated, and he laughed awkwardly. But her question was like a plea, an attempt to bridge the gulf between them. "On Saturday nights a fellow goes off somewhere around the city. The girls you run into on Saturday nights—oh, well,—" he went on, feeling miserable. "That stuff is a way of relaxing. Girls you don't watch yourself with," he tried to explain, feeling wretched that they were at the end of something. "Soon we'll both be leaving here, won't we?" he asked.

"Nobody likes to leave," she said weakly. And suddenly she didn't know whether she was in love with Tom Lane or whether she was in love with the life she had lived here the last four years. With a quick furtive eagerness she looked around at the lights gleaming in the windows, at the skyline with its familiar towers. Soon it would all be wrenched away from her. It would all be drained out of her life, and why? Why? Because she was a good scholar, because she must get her degree. In less than an hour she must return to Annesley Hall to plug at her books and make sure that she would separate herself forever from these places. If only Tom hadn't quoted that line from Emily Dickinson! She wanted to cry out her agonized protest that this kind of separation and this kind of energy and discipline should be required from her on such a spring night when the breeze was so soft and the stars so warm and close.

CHAPTER NINE

ND Tyndall too was beginning to find the time of approaching separation surprisingly painful. That year the Historical Club, a selective club for chosen men from the various colleges to discuss the affairs of the day, had its last meeting of the year at the home of Sir Joseph Flavelle, at the corner of the west crescent and Avenue Road. The Historical Club used to meet in these homes around the Park, and the host would always have the privilege of making a speech before serving the refreshments. Tyndall had attended this meeting at the Flavelle home with Tom Lane; and when they came out, and Tom offered to walk back to Hart House with him, Tyndall took his arm eagerly.

"Tom, I've got an idea," he said earnestly. "I wish you'd think about it. It would change your whole life, although it might require you to stay around here another year."

"Go ahead, sir. What is it?"

"Tom, why don't you try for a Rhodes Scholarship? A few

years at Oxford would be wonderful. You'd love it. You'd get along there. You'd really be at home."

"But wait a minute, sir," Tom said, starting to laugh. "I'd have no chance at a Rhodes Scholarship. I haven't got the scholastic standing. You forget, sir, I'm just a pass student. They wouldn't take me seriously."

"Of course they would, Tom," the Warden insisted doggedly. "They couldn't help it. You have the athletic requirements, the general interests, and even if you're from the pass course, well, there's the oral examination. You'd make an impression, Tom."

"No! I don't think so," Tom said, and he was confused. "Scholastically, I wouldn't rate."

"I've already talked to people, Tom."

"I'd have two strikes on me, Mr. Tyndall. I know fellows who'll go after the Rhodes Scholarship."

"But Oxford, Tom, is just the thing for a man like you."

"I'm not so sure of that," Tom said, and he looked troubled.

"You wouldn't want to go to Oxford, Tom?"

"Going to Oxford would be wonderful," Tom agreed, "especially if I were planning to teach, or go in for politics, or any number of things, but I've been thinking I'd like to take a shot at being a writer, Mr. Tyndall."

"But surely, Tom, you are aware of Oxford with its great tradition in English literature. Why, it would be magnificent for you," Tyndall said quickly. "I'm surprised you don't see it at once, Tom."

"It's rather hard to explain," Tom said. He shrugged and smiled and the words wouldn't come easily because he was now talking about something secret and close to his heart. "All a writer has, if he is any good, Mr. Tyndall, is his own eyes and his own ears," he went on. "Maybe I'm afraid of being seduced by the grandeurs and beauties of Oxford. Even around here I

114

n recognize the Oxford men, and they're not like me. I see ings the way I do because I grew up around here. It's all I ve, but it's mine. If I keep it I'll at least be trying to look at e world in my own way. That's the way it is, Mr. Tyndall."

"I see. Yes, I see what you mean," Tyndall said, his voice soft d apologetic. There was a little silence and Lane believed at he had wounded his friend for he could see that he was barrassed. But Tyndall was more than embarrassed. As he ughed and smiled awkwardly and linked his arm under Lane's ⸱ was trying to conceal in this gesture of affection his own eling of guilt. He was still making the mistake he had made hen he first came to Toronto. He wanted Lane to go to Oxford r the wrong reasons. He had gone on assuming with an un- tting snobbishness that a talented student like Lane was too od for his own Toronto environment and ought to be given e chance to flower somewhere else. And he was ashamed, but e proper kind of an apology was too difficult to make.

"I must seem like an awful fraud to you, Tom," he said vkwardly.

"A fraud? Why, sir?"

"I don't seem to have your feeling for this place."

"Why, you've really got more than I have, sir," Tom said.

"Well, thanks, Tom," he said sincerely. "Good night."

"Good night, Mr. Tyndall."

When Tyndall got back to Hart House a letter was there om Miss Hallam. It was quite a letter. It opened in a cold rmal style, but then it became the passionate outburst of a oman who believed she had been rejected for someone or mething else. She had long ago believed his story that he had tle respect for the University in which he worked, she wrote, it now she had come to the conclusion that he was a weak man ho no longer had the resolution to separate himself from a community that baffled him and only brought out the malice in his heart. Surely he could not feel at ease. Surely he felt hypocritical at Toronto. He could have come home, he could have taken the position her father had recommended; he would have been among his own people. Instead, he had let himself be swallowed up; he was lost, forever lost in the place he had called a big impersonal machine. She wrote eloquently. He was, no doubt, content to become a well-oiled nut or a bolt in his big machine. All his excuses only justified his lack of decision. And then, as if ashamed of her passion, the last paragraph of the letter became cold and formal again. An Auckland merchant whom she had known all her life, she wrote, wanted to marry her, and she found him attractive and she would not write to Tyndall again.

This letter, this sudden separation from someone who was a part of his life, shocked Tyndall, who had been reading it as he went along the corridor. Suddenly he stopped and sighed and was bewildered by his vast indecision. The letter had come at the wrong time. He had read it just after that conversation with Lane which had left him feeling apologetic and ashamed. Suddenly he wished that he had never come to Toronto. From the time he had come there, as Miss Hallam had implied, he had gone around wearing his own mask while trying to peer under the masks of others. Turning suddenly he rushed out. He wanted to feel the night air against his face. He felt lonely. All he had to do, he knew, was to write to Miss Hallam and say he was coming home, but as he headed aimlessly toward the park he knew with an amazed certainty that he would never go home.

If he had any real affection for the place it would be different, but he was always on the outside looking in and therefore lonely. Thousands of students passed through Hart House and he shared and directed their activities; he knew personally a

116

hundred men in the various departments but he had always felt cut off from them. So why had he stayed there? Because he was interested and unsatisfied. That damnable itch of curiosity and unsatisfied wonder had made him like a man with the artistic temperament who is always self-consciously observing and wondering, always separated. He had never been as lonely as he was now, wandering listlessly across the park.

It was the hour when the life of the University is all drawn into little rooms. Lights burn in the residences, lights blaze in the laboratories down at College Street. The personal lives and the personal dreams of a thousand university men are played out in these lonely lighted rooms. The whole neighbourhood has hundreds of such rooms, along St. Joseph, up St. George, along Madison and Huron.

It was the hour when a student is finished with his books. Having come from a small town he now sits around in a room in a big strange city, with no one to walk in on him, no place to go, no money to take a girl anywhere and nothing to do but warm himself with the ambition that he brought with him from his home town. In one room above Bloor a philosophy student is making a few dollars reading aloud to a blind professor. But his mind wanders; he sees himself going, when he is through reading, to his room on St. Mary Street, where his eyes will be so tired he won't want to read and there will be only the four walls and the noise of the cars rattling over Bay Street and the low rumble and whirl of the city in its nightly motion around him. And a chemistry professor, who has dashed home for his evening meal and a few moments with his children before rushing out to his car and driving back to College Street and his lab, is now taking a nap on the cot in the lab. Soon he will get up and go on with his research, driving his students as hard as he drives himself. The neighbours, hearing him returning home at two

117

o'clock, believe that he has been seeing another woman. No one believes the story of the lonely lab where he follows his hunches. It is a solitary life . . . But in a room north of Bloor, with the door locked, a young English professor, who has cut himself off from his wife and children while he pores over the poetry of Blake, seeking the truth behind the riddle of the prophetic words and wanting to give them meaning, shares this same loneliness. The lonely rooms of lonely men following their private hunches and their dreams. It did not occur to Tyndall that he, wandering in the park, was one of them. He had only his own minor problem; he would have been too embarrassed to explain it to any of these men. It would sound like the aberration of a stubborn man. A philosopher struggles a lifetime to make a system; a poet grasps a unity in a flash. Tyndall had merely wanted to discover a certain harmony and a tone in the institution he worked for, or to understand why he could not see them. With a wry smile he sighed, dug his hands deep in his pockets and felt that he had been like a painter commissioned to paint a little section of a great city wall; along with a thousand others working on the same vast mysterious mural, he had been forbidden to leave his work and withdraw to a point where he could see how it blended into the master design, and of course he had been always whispering and conniving with other little painters, trying to get them to dovetail their sections into some kind of pattern.

CHAPTER TEN

UT Tyndall had no idea that his habit of poking his nose into everything had endeared him to so many. His curiosity about individual students and Faculty members made them feel that their lives and their work had a remarkable importance. At any hour in the afternoon he could be seen dashing across the campus, turning unexpectedly into the little red school house or the Physics building, always wearing a jacket and an odd pair of pants, his shoulders held well back, his pipe belching smoke. All who saw him smiled affectionately. He would dive into one of these buildings as if something momentous had occurred to him.

In the Physics building which is just below Convocation Hall he would have pleasant conversation with the research men who enjoyed his amateur enthusiasm; they liked feeling that their work was being discovered by a layman. Of course, his explanations of his interest sometimes made him sound a little comical. He believed that the physicist was restoring a sense of mystery and wonder to the modern world. "He may be right at that," they said. "But he sounds as if he has been reading too many Sunday supplements." He wanted to know if anything had been done in their department that had never been done anywhere else on earth, and when they told him that their research men, working under J. C. McLennan, a remarkable organizer, had reproduced for the first time in a laboratory the green of the northern lights, he was delighted. "Ah, how appropriate. The northern lights. Canada!" he cried. "Why, it ought to have been done here." So it was a pleasure to talk to him about spectroscopy, about the hyperline structure in the spectra of thallium and bismuth, as if they were sure he understood them, or about how Canada had become the centre for electron microscopy. They encouraged him to brush up on his mathematics, which he tried to do.

But when he raised a question which to him as a layman seemed important they were often puzzled. He had a notion he had picked up somewhere about the quantum theory's being a death blow to the mechanistic theory of the universe; it had implication concerning freedom of action and free will, he insisted. When they explained patiently that they were physicists and not philosophers, he looked disgusted, and then they made little jokes about him. Professor H—— liked to tell how he had mentioned idly to Tyndall that he looked forward to the days when the research worker in physics would develop a new language based entirely on mathematical formula, and Tyndall, pounding the bowl of his pipe angrily on the arm of the chair, burst out, "Good heavens, man! aren't there too many special languages now? The whole language is going to be turned into a series of special jargons." Of course he didn't get the point. How was a research worker going to communicate with another research worker? That was their point, wasn't it?

By this time, of course, he assumed that he was merely immersed in his work. The old habit of enquiry was there, though, like the mechanical, inevitable, but unobserved working of a part of his mind. He was like a man who had got into the habit of picking up pieces of string and couldn't stop and was no longer aware he was doing it. He would be going about his work, functioning beautifully around Hart House, and then the sight of an interesting new face, a snatch of conversation overheard, would make him turn and draw close. It was his job, he believed, to be concerned about the thousands of students who wandered through Hart House. He got special tutors for some, he loaned money to one boy who couldn't pay his fees. And without realizing it, he became for Joe Boyle, a philosophy student at St. Mike's, a beloved guide to the great world.

For some years previously there were two opinions at St. Mike's concerning the relationship of the college with the rest of the University. Some believed the college should develop its own cultural pattern within its own walls; others thought the lives of the students might be enriched if blended more with the student life of the University as a whole. In those days the new college buildings were being built facing the park, and Joe Boyle lived most of his life in the old gray brick buildings with the primly Gothic touch, on Bay Street. In his first year he had roomed on the Jewish flat, then he had moved down to more comfortable quarters on the Irish flat.

That dusty, weedy, sandy athletic field behind the college, which has been so important to so many St. Mike's men, was used by Boyle as a promenade, for he was not athletic. That field was often so crowded with football teams, all practising at the same time, that a player, getting his signals crossed, sometimes wondered if he wasn't practising in the Grand Central Station. But Boyle promenaded sedately along the margin of the field with young scholastics wearing their soutanes, and priests catching a little fresh air; and the dust blew in his eyes and the wind caught the soutanes of the scholastics.

Students came to St. Mike's from all over Canada and from many of the American states, and they wondered if they would become priests. But Joe Boyle had an appreciation of his special vocation before he came there. He intended to be a prime minister at Ottawa. You could see it in every gesture and intonation and in his appraisal of a hundred complicated situations.

Boyle's mind interested Tyndall, who had met him on a Hart House Committee, because it was so unlike Lane's. Boyle was never in an intellectual ferment. "Of course at St. Mike's we have our philosophy," Boyle used to say to Tyndall, as if it explained his calm assurance and his nice intellectual balance; he knew exactly what he wanted; he had an astonishing supply of quotations from St. Augustine and Aristotle which used to flabbergast his opponents in debate. He had that talent which is envied by all politicians, business men and administrators—good judgment. He wanted the University to train him to become a first-class cabinet minister. If the Ontario Legislature were in session he would go down to the Parliament Buildings, listen all afternoon and walk back across the park to his college with his slow stride while he refuted to his own satisfaction those speeches which had most annoyed him.

In his own college where his vast amiability made him popular he was watched with a wondering admiration. Everything was grist for his mill. He was a great admirer of Father Carr who had been Superior, and had deep respect for Father McCorkell, who had succeeded Father Carr. Boyle was impressive because he had character while being able to accept easily the college discipline. He gave no one any trouble. He went to mass every morning, was attentive on the retreats, led the students' parliament and the cheering for the football team. Aristotle, St. Augustine and St. Thomas provided him with a fortification and with the arsenal of quotations that made him bewilderingly formidable. With his own college as a base he began to make sorties into the wider university world, using Tyndall as a guide and loving and respecting him.

His praise of Tyndall irritated some of the men sitting around in the Irish flat. He also tested the patience of the priests, but they wanted to see him get on in the world. They seemed to understand that when Boyle was walking up and down the margin of the muddy playground watching the football teams practise, he was dreaming of the world in which he had begun to walk with Tyndall. The whole University was opening up to Boyle as a complicated political training ground. From the fastness of his own college he looked out over the other colleges as Napoleon, a boy in Corsica, must have looked at France. Boyle noticed how Tyndall dressed, he observed his easy social grace; and what was most inspiring of all, it seemed to him that Tyndall recognized his, Boyle's, talent and ambition, for any time a political figure visited Hart House, Boyle was invited there to meet him. Tyndall took Boyle to lunch with him at the York Club. He would sometimes take him out with him to the houses of important people. He urged him to join the Historical Club; he saw him become an intercollegiate debater. There weren't many girls in Boyle's life. Instead there were Aristotle, St. Thomas, Father Carr, Father McCorkell, Sir Wilfrid Laurier, R. B. Bennett . . . and Tyndall. The girls from St. Joseph's and Loretto, who danced and drank tea with the boys from St. Michael's at Newman Club on St. George Street every Saturday afternoon, didn't see much of Boyle for some time. The ladies of Loretto and the girls from St. Jo's didn't have a chance to appreciate Mr. Boyle until his fourth year, when he came over to the club quietly, seemed to put his arms warmly around everybody, and was quickly and inevitably elected president.

But it was the interest of Tyndall, a man of the world, that fascinated Boyle. Why was Tyndall always anxious to help him? One day, for instance, he said to Boyle, "I'd like to see you do a little more imaginative reading, Joe. The contemporary writers or even, let's say, the Greek dramatists. There's the world of the library, the world of books."

"Books," said Boyle with his warm smile. "Hm." He had a kind of elephantine humour which sometimes puzzled Tyndall. "Don't you know, Mr. Tyndall, that books can drive a man crazy?"

"I'm serious, Joe."

"Oh, so am I," Boyle said, and he seemed to be quite serious.

"But isn't that an odd remark for a university man?"

"I'm being literal," Boyle insisted. "You say I should use the University library more. I give you my word that right down in the main library there's a man who's gone crazy. Books have done it, Mr. Tyndall."

"Who is he, Joe?"

"I won't tell you his name, Mr. Tyndall. It wouldn't be fair," he said solemnly.

He had sounded so ponderously sincere that Tyndall believed him, and from then on whenever he heard a rumour of someone around there being downright queer he would wonder if this could be the man Boyle had mentioned. Boyle's elephantine humour was usually expressed with such a plausible solemnity that you never could tell.

And the University library, that weathered old stone building with its rear wing foundations buried deep in the valley, was becoming so crowded it often resembled a basement bargain shop. Any kind of hysteria was possible there. The library had been built to accommodate a university of about two thousand students. Now it had about seven thousand customers, who were so badly accommodated through the lack of space and of necessary books that it could be easily taken for a psychiatric centre; it produced irritations, frustrations, and a certain paranoiac mania. A student or a professor who couldn't get the book he had been seeking, or who had to stand in line, could easily believe he was being cunningly persecuted. And so Tyndall would find himself glancing at the library every time he passed it. Once he did go in and had a little talk with the librarian, who seemed sane enough. He kept wondering if Boyle had been pulling his leg.

Then came the convocation in the early summer when Boyle was graduated with distinction. On such a day the graduates stream across the campus from their separate colleges. They come carrying their gowns, heading for that domed hall. The Chancellor in his black and yellow gown and the President in his silver and blue gown are there on the dais, and you might say that all there is to it is a few speeches and the reading-out of the names of the graduates, who march on to the platform, shake hands with the Chancellor and receive the symbols of their degrees. But it is only when he comes outside into the sunlight, where the relatives are standing in little groups, or where the girls of some of the students are happy in their new summer dresses, that a more wistful graduate than Boyle begins to feel a kind of emptiness in his little triumph, for there is the campus and there the towers of the colleges, the old green trees and the grass soft in the sunlight; there the paths where he has walked in the good years of his life.

But Boyle, who had come out of the hall with Tyndall, knew he wasn't going to lose anything. He expected to go on to Osgoode Hall and study law. He expected to appear every week at Newman Hall, he expected to visit the Warden as often as possible in Hart House. There was to be a splendid continuity to his life. Yet he did turn to Tyndall and with a manly directness he said simply, "I owe a lot to you, Mr. Tyndall. I want to thank you."

"No. No. You owe nothing whatever to me, Joe," Tyndall said. "But there's something I often intended to ask you, Joe. Do you remember telling me there was a crazy man in the library?"

"Good heavens!" Boyle said in astonishment. "That was months ago. Why did that stick in your mind, Mr. Tyndall?"

"Well," Tyndall began with an embarrassed smile. "I like men around a university who can be a little mad."

"Why, it's simple," Boyle said, chuckling deeply and enormously pleased at the lasting success of his little joke. "You know the school book fable about the horse and the rider? A nail was lost from the horse's shoe. As a result of the nail the shoe was lost, as a result of the shoe the horse was lost, and with the horse lost the rider was lost?"

"Of course, of course," Tyndall said impatiently.

"Well, that's the way it is with the books at the library. That's all I meant, Mr. Tyndall. As a result of there being no room down there a book is lost, and with the book lost, the student is lost, and with the student lost he doesn't show up at his lecture or is late waiting for the book, and the whole rhythm of the University is broken."

"Excellent. Excellent. But who is the crazy man, Joe?"

"Why, the fellow down there who has to place five books on a shelf where there is only room for one. Wouldn't it drive you crazy doing that night after night, Mr. Tyndall?" And Boyle burst into laughter.

"Oh, yes, it would," Tyndall said, smiling wanly.

As they began to walk across the campus Boyle said, "Mr.

Tyndall, I never quite figured out why you took such an interest in me." Moved himself, he wanted to show the older man how grateful he was.

"Well, I don't know, Joe," Tyndall said softly, squinting a little because of the last of the strong sunlight. He also had an odd meditative little smile. "I suppose it was like watching a man pick up his equipment, or getting used to his tools."

"I don't know what you mean, Mr. Tyndall."

"Well, let me repeat that line of Emerson's with which he greeted the appearance of Walt Whitman. 'I salute you at the beginning of a great career.' Yes, Joe."

Moved by Boyle's gratitude Tyndall found difficulty in explaining his interest any further. "Did you know Tom Lane?" he asked.

"Not well, I heard him debate. He was a few years ahead of me, Mr. Tyndall."

"Well, for him the University meant the flowering of the private life."

"Yes, go on, sir."

"For you it's the university for the flowering of the public life."

"Oh, I see."

"It was beautiful, Joe, to see you come here with your dream and use every hour to make the dream real. I used to wonder if you weren't truly the Toronto man. I used to ask people if there was a Toronto Varsity man. But now I see that Toronto is only a little part of you. I think, Joe, you have most of the typical Canadian virtues. Yes, you belong to the country, Joe. You have all the national political virtues—caution, judgment and prudence. You were at home here, Joe, just as you'll be at home anywhere in the country. It was interesting, very interesting to see you flower here . . ."

"But aren't those good things, Mr. Tyndall?" Boyle asked, looking surprised.

"Wonderful things," Tyndall agreed, but there was an ironic twist to his mouth that would have wounded Boyle if he hadn't felt so sure of Tyndall's real affection for him . . .

CHAPTER ELEVEN

DURING a depression a university is a perfect refuge. The registration increases. So it was now; many young men and women, who had nowhere else to go, came to the University and believed that their lives were being shaped by economic disaster. The place was expanding. On College Street was the new Connaught Laboratory, a fine brick building. And also on College, opposite the General Hospital, was the Banting Institute, a five-storey red brick building. And they were building the new St. Michael's College and the Mediaeval Institute facing the park. In a slow glacial-like movement the University began to expand along College, up St. George and around the Park; and the School of Graduate Studies had a record enrolment. At the old Stadium on Bloor Street they were watching a new style of football. The boys were throwing forward passes, and some of the old football mentors were muttering angrily and pulling at their moustaches and talking about the Americanization of everything.

133

There was, of course, a sudden shift in the fashion in learning. The courses in sociology became popular. Girls, and young men who didn't want to be full-fledged sociologists, concentrated on psychology. In the newspapers the scientists were no longer quoted about remedies for all the world's ills. The psychiatrist and the psychologist were having their hour. That pink-cheeked and white-haired Victoria philosopher whom Tyndall had encountered a few years ago when he had lunched at Victoria, spoke of the "new learning". He viewed it with equanimity, he said, and was sure that in the fifteenth century he wouldn't have been opposed to the great Renaissance. It was possible that it was all the one thing. There was a rumour that those in authority at St. Michael's viewed the new learning uneasily, he said; this couldn't be verified.

Tyndall was having lunch one day with young Dr. J——, a professor of Anatomy. The young doctor had a quiet dignity that came out of his devotion to his work, but Tyndall had always felt in him a conflict between his intellectual convictions and his own conduct as a man. The young doctor had a gentle manner, he lived a good quiet life, he had the loftiest moral principles, but intellectually he was a mechanist, a behaviourist, and his impersonal view of life could be frightening. Tyndall had been talking about a lunch he had had with some people in the Connaught Laboratory and about how impressed he had been by the lively interest these people, concerned with production of products useful in preventive medicine, had taken in politics and the general human condition. Then he had asked his friend the doctor to tell him something about the Banting Institute. "Well, what do you want to know?" the doctor asked with a shrug. "It's simply part of the Medical School where research work is done," and he smiled as if Tyndall's interest were naïve, or as if Tyndall believed that the Institute was a magician's stronghold.

But he sounded so impersonal, so unwilling to be excited, that Tyndall felt again that old irritation. That little part of his own mind which was in a sense split off from the part which he used every hour, and which was still busily recording these irritating little observations and working away at the old problem, began to function instantly. He couldn't help it. Here again he was up against the old impersonal effacement.

"At least give me the bare facts," Tyndall prodded him.

"All right, wait till I put on my gold-braided hat and my uniform, and I'll show you around," the doctor said, grinning. "The main pathological museum is on the main floor. So are the cloak-rooms for students." He chanted in the flat voice of a tourists' guide. "An autopsy theatre for students is in the sub-basement. Now, ladies and gentlemen, we are on the main floor. Here they do the administrative laboratory- and research-work for the Department of Pathology. And yes, in the east wing there's a lecture room for two hundred students. They can show movies there. Let us hurry now to the second floor, Mr. Tyndall. Most of the space on the second floor is given over to the Department of Bacteriology. And there's a big laboratory with one hundred and fifty student places for the teaching of bacteriology and pathology. Now we slowly approach the third floor—the clinical departments, the administrative and research rooms and a library for clinical and pathological books . . . " He laughed because Tyndall was laughing, but he went on bravely. "On the fourth floor, pathological chemistry," he intoned. "A students' laboratory for that subject and clinical miscroscopy. On the fifth—oh, go down and see the place some day, Tyndall," he said, becoming bored with his act. "As I say, it's called the Banting Institute, but it might have been called something else. I think they did have another name in mind for it. How would you like to walk me down to the Anatomy building?"

"Of course," Tyndall said. But as they got up and got their hats and went out he still had the wondering smile. Once again he seemed to be close to an illumination—close to the missing factor in the pattern he had been seeking for years. So he held on to the young doctor's arm tightly as if afraid to let him get away. They walked along the drive and up the little hill to the crescent where they both bowed politely to the gray-haired man who was approaching. "How do you do. How do you do, Dr. Cody," they called to the President. They talked a little about Dr. Cody. When they got to the Anatomy building Tyndall, still reluctant to leave his friend, went on in with him, asking himself, "This lack of excitement, this effacement, what is it? A failure of the imagination?" His friend was capable of brilliant research work. Yet at lunch-time he had said that research laboratories all over the world kept in touch with each other. The discoveries they made were like a slow impersonal inevitable movement toward the ultimate desired fact. It was all impersonal, it all dovetailed, it was the scientific method, no one in particular was to be singled out for glory. The research workers, indeed, were the masked men.

"Why not go in and look around?" the young doctor said, pointing to the room near the door which was the Anatomical Museum. "You seem to be so interested in what goes on around here, Tyndall."

"I must get back," Tyndall said. But near the door was the glass case in which a hand and an arm were pickled in alcohol. The yellowish skin was drawn back, each bone, muscle and sinew was shown, and all the tissues, too.

"It seems to impress you, Tyndall," the young doctor said finally.

"It does," Tyndall said. "I suppose it's the mood I'm in. I was just thinking—in that arm and hand is a kind of knowledge that just make the Arts man feel futile when he suggests that the doctor should have the culture to deal with the whole of life. Don't you see what I mean?" he asked earnestly. "The mystery and wonder of life is laid open in that arm and hand. And it's what a doctor is dealing with all the time, isn't it?"

"Yes, that's right," his friend agreed, staring at the hand as he had never seen it before. Then he grinned. "But if a young doctor glanced at that arm you know all he would be concerned with? He'd simply wonder how he could sew it up." Then they laughed and shook hands.

"Well, so long, and thanks," Tyndall said. "Thanks very much."

"Thanks for what, Tyndall?"

"The information . . . Why, about the Banting Institute," Tyndall said with a smile that mystified the doctor.

With the brisk air of a man who had picked up a very useful piece of information which he would store away and use in his own good time, Tyndall walked away.

A little quarrel he had with an engineering professor was equally important to him. It was not really a quarrel. But it might easily have become a harsh and violent affair if Tyndall hadn't had his peculiar obsession.

On that November night Tyndall had gone to a lecture in Trinity College with his friend, the old and sour English professor from U.C., the embittered champion of a residence for University College, who had been retired two years ago. The old professor came to all these lectures because he had no place else to go. This particular lecture was one of a series on social conflicts in the modern world. Before an admiring crowd the lecturer, a tall thin handsome young cleric with a sociological point of view, was brilliantly examining the source of the international tensions. Tyndall and the irascible old English professor were sitting together in the middle of the appreciative audience. Tyndall, too, was appreciative, even though he couldn't understand why he had such a hard time following the lecturer's sentences. But the old professor, chewing on his moustache, mumbled bitterly. It was awfully embarrassing. The hoarse whispers could be heard across the hall. Those who had been listening raptly, turned and glared at the retired professor. It didn't disturb him at all. He was just as angry as they were and he kept up his fierce mumbling. "What a strange jargon! What does the man mean? Why doesn't he say what he means? I doubt if it has any meaning. Listen to him, Tyndall."

Yet it was a splendid lecture, immensely satisfying to the audience, and Tyndall, trying to silence his friend, whispered, "You and I are out of date. But if we listen we can pick it up."

But when the lecture was over and they were coming out the withered old professor was still muttering violently, "Tensions, techniques and dynamics. I heard him say it a dozen times. You heard him, too, Tyndall."

"It's the new learning," Tyndall said soothingly.

"It's the new barbarism," the old man muttered. "I'm ashamed of you, Tyndall, for being so receptive."

They had fallen in step with J. C. E——, the big good-natured professor from the School of Practical Science, who was smiling and winking at Tyndall and enjoying the old English teacher's indignation. When they had said good night outside on Hoskin, Tyndall and the engineer walked in step across the road and down the walk by Hart House. The engineer was on his way down to College Street. "Dear me," Tyndall said, half to himself, "everything is being made more technical these days. There seems to be such a craving for technical expression."

"Maybe it simply represents an effort to be exact," the engineer said mildly.

"Yes, possibly," Tyndall agreed. Still thinking out loud and forgetting whom he was with he sighed and said, "Soon we'll all be technicians, and then the jig is up."

"Oh, that's absurd, Tyndall," the engineer said sharply, his tone so challenging that Tyndall stopped and stared at him. They were now at the Memorial Tower. The full moon shed its light on the engineer's angry face.

"What did I say?" Tyndall asked innocently.

"Oh, that nonsense about the jig being up."

"But what did you think I meant?" Tyndall asked nervously, knowing the amiable engineer was ready to quarrel with him.

"I hear that kind of stupid remark every day," the big engineer said impatiently. "I know you, too, Tyndall. You're one of those wistful classics men. The humanities and so on, and that silly air of mourning about the ascendency of the technical men. I'm an engineer, Tyndall. I'm helping to turn out hundreds of young engineers, and your anachronistic old friend would like to say that we're barbarians because we don't think like you do. You're an anachronism yourself, Tyndall."

"Let's not be petty," Tyndall said coldly.

"It's time someone did a little blunt speaking around here, Tyndall."

"Surely we don't have to be insulting."

"The raw truth is, of course, insulting."

"I won't argue with you on your terms."

"Of course not. I'll pull you out of your dream. Am I supposed to believe that those intellectuals you admire who talk about beauty and get dizzy trying to define it, and who add a thousand footnotes to vague little theses about beauty, are the ones who can train men to live in our own time? What nonsense, Tyndall. At our school of architecture—by the way, Tyndall, did you know we had a school of architecture? Have you taken any interest

139

in it? There you get men trained in a practical relationship between utility and design, and the materials for the design."

"Don't take that tone to me," Tyndall said angrily.

"Don't lecture me, Tyndall," the engineer said harshly. "For a change you'll listen to me."

"I have no recollection of you ever having listened to me."

"Well, people like you, then. They're springing up like mushrooms. In the name of liberal arts. I suppose old Archimedes defending the harbour of Syracuse with little engineering feats wasn't one of the town's intellectuals. Well, the engineer's mind possesses the kind of training that permits him to help the human race to widen the whole range of human achievement."

"Nobody's attacking you," Tyndall said angrily. "Nobody at all." Then suddenly a thought struck him. Drawing back he stared at the engineer and then burst into laughter.

"Yes, do go on, please," he begged the engineer.

"Eh? What's this?"

"It just struck me why you are excited," Tyndall said, still laughing. "It's really your world and you know it. The engineers are on the ascendency everywhere. The whole of our civilization belongs to the technical man. The engineer isn't only in the lab in industry, he's now in the executive's chair, too. And you know it. But I think I know what's worrying you."

"Nothing's worrying me, Tyndall."

"Yes. The same thing that's been worrying me."

"Eh?"

"The lack of balance of things around here. Something missing in your own engineers, too, isn't that so?" Tyndall asked eagerly.

"Tyndall, I think—well, I think," the engineer began, standing now with his hands on his hips, his face in the moonlight blank and incredulous. "I waste my time, Tyndall. I think you're a little quaint. Good night. No hard feelings." And he turned away abruptly.

But he had convinced Tyndall that many of the professors, without realizing it, were sharing his problem with him. He began to go more often to the Faculty room.

It was true that some of the professors, sitting around in the Faculty room after lunch (when they have a chance to talk to each other), had commented upon the evenness of tone among them. With a kind of amusement mixed with resignation they had accepted and deplored it. There had been a time, some of them complained, when a university professor regarded himself as a man of intellect, bristling with ideas, who ought to assert by his very presence, his style of dressing and his flow of speech, that he wasn't a business man. In the old days a professor was expected to have a certain colour of his own, even if he showed it only in the way he tied his tie or wore his hat. In those days, the same ones said, the intellectual had a pride in his influence on the community. As the University got bigger and the research men and the engineers became a part of the industrial fabric of the country, their worth recognized by even the most practical industrialist, they found themselves completely at home in the industrial world; they had no desire to be mistaken for quaint figures with a special glamour of their own. The Arts man, in his deportment and speech, now wanted to declare that he too could be mistaken for a business man. He could walk down Bay Street with his brief-bag and happily be mistaken for a bond salesman.

A history professor once complained that few professors enter politics, few of them publicly express strong opinions. In Toronto the professors have about the same social rating as doctors or lawyers. They find their friends among their own colleagues or in the professions. In the main they are quiet, modest, hard working, and often very tired. They have too many students and not much time for their own creative scholarship, and so when you meet one of them at a party you get the impression that he will be happy if you don't plunge him into an intellectual discussion that will exhaust some of his desperately needed energy.

They had this deprecating view of themselves, and yet among them were men who had written textbooks used all over America. Some had written poetry, some had written critical works, some had written histories that had made them famous; but they were not quite sure they were famous. In the whole country there was not a group of scholars to equal them, but, of course, no one would admit it.

It always seemed to Tyndall that they had a desire to mask their noble achievement in scholarship, to hope almost that it wouldn't be noticed. They didn't get excited about each other; they hardly mentioned each other's attainments; they walked circumspectly in the twilight with their neat business suits and their brief-bags. In fact, they hardly knew each other. There were so many of them that one could spend ten years there and scarcely be aware of his colleagues. Even in the Faculty dining-room a man from the Economics Department would be found eating with a colleague from the same department. One of them would say, "Oh, yes, I know whom you mean. I know his name well, but I've never met him. I'd like to sit down with him some day, but he usually eats with men in his own department." They all wanted to meet each other, but they were too hurried; they had huge classes.

The depression had separated them a little more from their students; money wasn't available for those little social gatherings in their own homes.

One day Tyndall went into the Faculty common-room. His

friend the old mathematician was there on a chair but he seemed to be dozing blissfully after lunch. Tyndall sat down, lit his pipe and listened to a history professor, a mild, sharp-minded, un-ruffled man of fifty-five with a smooth bald head, who was talking to a young curly-haired colleague in the English Department.

"You may start lecturing to the engineers, I hear," said the young English professor.

"So they say."

"I suppose it will fit in with C. R. Young's dream of liberaliz-ing the Engineering course."

"Well, I don't think you're going to liberalize the engineers. They're a pretty hearty bunch, and they're not going to pay much attention to us. Besides I've heard them shout so long that they can demolish forty beers that I've come to believe it," the history professor said. He obviously felt overwhelmed by too many engineers. "What would a few casual lectures in English amount to?" he asked with a shrug. "It would probably be a course in letter writing."

"These technical men now are well trained," said his younger colleague. "You've got to admit it. They get everything. They can get the money because they can show results."

"Just the same," said the history professor, "I distrust the wisdom of this plan that would mix up the engineers with the arts. Let their own men influence them. They're the ones that really influence them anyway. After all they have their own style of thinking."

"But surely you don't want to keep these men in different compartments, do you?" Tyndall asked.

"Well, why not, Tyndall?"

"Why the passion for splitting up the Toronto personality?"

"Poor Tyndall. I can remember when he asked me if I could pick out a Toronto man."

"And what did you say?" asked the English professor.

"I told him I couldn't."

"Maybe I was innocent," Tyndall agreed. "But I still think people around here like to—well, let's say, keep out of sight."

"I don't know that it's so bad at that," said the historian. "When I was in New York I seemed to be surrounded by scholars, scientists, historians and research men who were always proclaiming that they were the greatest scholars in the world and I must say that I got tired of it and felt uncomfortable. I wanted to get back here."

"Where you could become anonymous," Tyndall said quickly. "Why, that's it," he repeated. "Where you could become anonymous."

"Yes, I'm your anonymous man, Tyndall."

"But a whole university can't be anonymous. It's got to stand for something, surely."

"I doubt very much, Tyndall," the history professor said finally, "whether you can ever get a picture of this University as a whole. It's too big. Too many cultural influences, Tyndall. Too many branches of knowledge. We ought to be able to name the thing for what it is, but we can't get far enough away from it." Cupping his chin in his hand, he frowned and pondered, and the English professor, too, was silent. "Well, maybe this is what it amounts to," the history professor said with a sigh. "Maybe each one of us is like a coral ant, adding his own little driblet and enlargement and utterly unable to get outside and see the coral island."

"A professor around here a coral ant," said the English professor. "What a comforting thought."

"Yes, a sad role for a professor."

"To see the thing as a whole is like asking for a mystical experience," said the English professor, standing up and looking at his wrist watch.

"And the mystical experience may be more in Tyndall's line than in mine," agreed the history professor. "Well, I'm walking down to Baldwin House. So long, Tyndall. Think of us as coral ants."

"I'll still think of the coral," Tyndall said, and he laughed, but only to conceal a sudden exasperation. It seemed to him that the mild-mannered, self-possessed historian ought to have been one of the Faculty men who would refuse to accept the anonymous role. In fact he was one of those who were not anonymous: his opinions were important; he was often quoted in other cities; he irritated many people; he had his own influence. And yet such a man was content to think of himself as a coral ant.

When they had gone he moved over to the window. In a little while the two professors came out and went slowly down the walk in the sunlight. It was a clear spring day. The girls on the paths were wearing bright-coloured jackets. Yes, Tyndall thought, if he went on seeking unity or trying to see the thing as a whole, he would become the University's philosopher, but then, indeed, he would be isolated. No other philosopher around there would agree with him. They couldn't agree with each other. Could the Thomist, Dr. Phelan, agree with Dr. Anderson, the Platonist?

"Tyndall, do come here a moment," called the old mathematician who with one eye open had been listening to the history professor. Even now as Tyndall approached he kept only this one sharp eye open; his hands remained folded blissfully across his chest; and his head rested on the back of the sofa. He looked like a quizzical one-eyed gnome. "Tyndall, I was thinking about you," he said, as Tyndall sat down beside him. "You and your missing link," he chuckled. "However, I have a little thought that may help you. This year our graduate school has a record enrolment. Why should it be so?"

"The relentless quest for the Ph.D., I suppose."

"Come, Tyndall, I'm supposed to be the cynic around here. If graduates from the United States come here, it must be for some one reason."

"The excellence of teachers, or good courses."

"Exactly, Tyndall. The reputation of men." He sounded distressingly pompous. As he got older he felt that he had far more time to be garrulous, and he plainly enjoyed himself. "A great university in the Middle Ages was like a travelling circus," he went on. "Students would go for five hundred miles to hear a particular scholar. Men, Tyndall, men. Don't you understand?" he asked in that dry mocking tone, with that amused little twisted smile, as if he had known for years what was bothering Tyndall. Suddenly he sat up, both eyes wide open; his voice grew soft and strangely comforting. "You know, Tyndall, you're such a hopeful man—almost incurable."

"How so?"

"You expect life to have some meaning."

"Why, yes, I suppose so."

"But supposing you could see it had no meaning at all."

"It must have a meaning."

"But that's what's been bothering you around here, Tyndall. You look out over our Toronto University—in all its fields—and you see that it's a microcosm of our modern life. It ought to have a design, eh, Tyndall? But supposing you realized it had no design at all. No meaning at all. Oh, yes," he said, getting up and stretching comfortably. "A notion with very satisfactory ramifications."

"Yes. Yes. Providing you really mean it," Tyndall said thoughtfully. He walked to the cloakroom with the mathematician, watched him bend and gasp for breath, his face reddening, as he put on his rubbers. Had this happy, witty old man explained the source of his happiness? Of course, if there were no design, no meaning, well, nothing would have to be justified, nothing would have to be related to a goal beyond itself. In a sense one was free. It was possible that the impersonal attitude which had such general approval was simply a recognition that life had no meaning.

Tyndall and the old mathematician were walking along the corridor, and at the end they parted and Tyndall stood there listening to the thump of the professor's rubbers on the stairs. If he had seen from the beginning that there was no design, could be no pattern, any more than there was a vast design to life itself, how free he might have felt here in Toronto from the beginning. What a liberation! All one had to do was make one's own little pattern; one was in charge of one's own life. On the campus there could be eight thousand little patterns. He could have married Miss Hallam. He could have had such an easy untroubled life.

And then as he turned away from the stairs, not knowing whether he was excited or disappointed, there came to his mind a picture of himself standing near the Parliament Buildings in the rain watching a stocky medical student in a trench coat coming down the cinder path. It was like his memory jogging him impatiently. It was a very bright picture seen in a flash. The boy who had read the Osler lectures.

CHAPTER TWELVE

HE old mathematician had said that when men came from other lands and other universities to do post-graduate work then Toronto would be truly known for what it was. Now, indeed, they were coming. Tyndall didn't have a chance to meet many of them because few shared in the undergraduate student life. They had a room of their own in the University library. Some stayed at College residences, some in little rooms close to the University. What the old mathematician had meant was that these pilgrim scholars from afar would come to Toronto if they believed that the tuition there would lead them to a degree which would be honoured throughout the world. In the long run, then, the post-graduate students would come to Toronto because of the teachers who were there. It was strange, Tyndall often thought, that the most cynical of all his friends was the one who kept repeating, "men, men". There was a nice paradoxical touch to this that delighted Tyndall.

He was in the barber shop one day getting a haircut. Leaning back with his eyes closed he had been listening only to the click of the scissors on the back of his neck (he would never let the barber use the clippers on his neck), and then he had heard the voices of strangers with American accents, two dissimilar American accents. The two strangers were there on the chairs waiting their turn. One, plump and blue-eyed, was losing his hair, the other, dark and lean, had big restless deep-set brown eyes.

"Where are you from, gentlemen?" Tyndall asked when he got out of the chair.

"I'm from New York. I was at Harvard. My name is Williams," said the tall dark one.

"And mine is Adams," said the plump one. "Chicago. And the University of Chicago."

"Doing post-graduate work, I take it."

"Yes, sir."

"I see. And may I ask what was the attraction up here?"

"The Medieval Institute," said the dark one.

"And Gilson and Maritain," said the other.

"Oh, yes, of course, the French Thomist philosophers. Their work is known to you, and you want to teach, I suppose."

"I had heard Gilson of the Collège de France, and I had read Maritain in Paris," said the Chicago man. "When we heard they were coming here, well, this was the place to come."

"I've been in France myself," Tyndall said. "Look here, Father M—— over at St. Mike's is a friend of mine. I was thinking of asking him over for dinner. I'd like you two to come along with him. It must be a little lonely for you."

Making them completely at ease with him, he shook hands, and hoped he had made two new friends. The fact that they had come to Toronto on an academic journey that had really begun in France deeply impressed him. Up to this time he hadn't paid much attention to the establishment of the Medieval Institute at St. Michael's, which had been the realization of a dream of Father Henry Carr. Father Carr and his Basilian Colleagues had wanted to have at the University a school for the study of the philosophy of the Middle Ages which would be supported by the best Medieval library in North America; it was to have also the teaching of the most famous Catholic medieval philosophers. This Institute had been established so quietly at Toronto under Dr. Gerald Phelan, that a number of Faculty men were hardly aware it was there.

The two Americans came to dinner and were a bit reticent at first; they weren't quite sure what Tyndall expected of them. But Father M—— was such a slow-talking affable companion, with such a contagious boyish laugh, that everything went easily. Father M—— at that time was forty-seven, and his hair was graying, but he looked as young and healthy as the plump American from Chicago. He was one of those peculiarly relaxed men with great repose, and was always asking innocent questions as if he didn't know anything. At the dinner he questioned Tyndall, he let the two Americans explain Maritain to him, he let Tyndall explain the poetry of Catullus; and he made them all feel they had enriched his life. St. Michael's College was in his bones; he had gone there to high school, had taken his degree there, and now was a professor.

Father M—— had to leave early, and when he had gone, Adams, the Chicago man, asked, "Would you mind telling me what you make of him, Mr. Tyndall?"

"A charming man. He's well liked around here. What bothers you about him?"

"It's that comforting simplicity of his. All these Basilians are so unpretentious—but Father M—— Well, I can't make up my mind. Is there real depth there?"

"You'll find him bobbing up lecturing in the Institute," his friend said. "And you'll be surprised. I tell you he's a character right out of Stendhal." And while they argued Tyndall was chuckling to himself. They were strangers, as he had been a stranger, and he knew how they were baffled by Father M——'s intellectual self-effacement proper to Toronto.

After that night Tyndall began to talk enthusiastically about the Institute with professors in the Faculty room. Some of the philosophers only exasperated him. His tall sharp-tongued portly friend, the Platonist, took him consolingly by the arm and said, "I don't know what you expect to find over there, Tyndall, but I'll tell you what you'll get. Simply warmed-over Aristotle," and he chuckled and hurried away. Another philosopher, whom Tyndall had asked about Jacques Maritain, shrugged and said, "Well, is he a philosopher or an apologist?" But Tyndall, who was used to this kind of caution, would smile and explain he was delighted that men of ideas, even if they were alien to him, could come to a school as did the thirteenth-century scholars and bring their followers with them. He was a romantic, the tall and portly philosopher said. "No," cried Tyndall. "If Spengler had come here, if Whitehead came here, if Toynbee gave a series of lectures here I'd be just as interested. It gives us a place on the world stage. I like to think of Gilson and Maritain, from Paris, walking across our campus. It enriches the life here, gives colour and the clash of ideas."

He attended a Gilson lecture with a French professor from Trinity. Here he met again his two American friends. Afterwards they had a cup of coffee in a Bloor Street restaurant. It could have been that he was charmed by novelty, but it excited him to be sitting in the little quick lunch, getting embroiled in a conversation about Beaudelaire, Péguy, Leon Bloy and the Cathedral at Chartres. His new friends talked eagerly. They were aglow with ideas. "Don't you know that men in the twelfth entury would tear the skin off a man with tongs for the sake f an idea?" Adam explained fiercely.

When they were exhausted, the tall one, Williams, from Harvard, leaned back and said in a whisper, accompanied by a beautiful smile, "Notre Baudelaire," and the other smiled gently, too, and it was as if they were whispering the words of a litany. Tyndall, holding his mug of coffee in both hands, also smiled but remained silent and wondering. He had suddenly felt the impact of another culture slashing into the pattern of the University of Toronto, and though these two voices expressed the enchantment of a French Catholic culture, other voices would come and be heard more and more in the Basilian College and then echo, even if faintly, in the other colleges too.

This perception ought to have worried him, Tyndall knew. It only complicated more than ever the Toronto cultural pattern. Just why it didn't worry him he tried to figure out on the walk home. Was it because he loved variety and the personal gesture? he asked himself. If he were being seduced now by that love, wasn't it because he had found variety lacking in the life around him? If it were so then the pleasure he was getting from his conversations with these Americans was the kind of pleasure he had often missed in Toronto. It all fitted in, he thought, smiling to himself.

He had missed the excitement that came from being close to a young fellow like Lane of Trinity, who rushed headlong at ideas. His new friendship with Adams, the plump balding student from Chicago, became such a sharing of the tumult of ideas that he was often shaken and exhausted. That winter at ten in the evening he would walk over to Elmsley Place towards the big house at the head of the little street where Adams had his room, and he would look up to see if the light was burning. He would whistle softly. The sound of his own whistling always embarrassed him and he would look around as if he expected one of the Basilians to rush out and drive him away. In a few moments he would see Adams' shadow against the window as he stood up. Then the window would be opened, Adams would whistle and in a few moments come down with his overcoat collar turned up, his hat pulled down over his eyes, looking tired, troubled and unhappy. He was writing a thesis on Aesthetics, St. Augustine's idea of beauty, and of course he wanted to read all the other books on aesthetics ever written. On the way up to Bloor Street for his cup of coffee before he went to bed, his mind would be charged with ideas. Sitting down Tyndall would say, "You don't look too happy tonight, Adams, what's the trouble?"

"What's the trouble," Adams would answer as if he wanted to shout at him. "I'm tired. I'm trying to possess the thought of St. Augustine. For the next two years I want to think, feel and breathe like St. Augustine. I want to understand every line he said about the beautiful." An embittered look would come on his face while Tyndall smiled sympathetically. "The trouble is he didn't say directly an awful lot about the beautiful. Even St. Thomas didn't say very much directly. 'That which gives pleasure at sight . . .'"

"That definition would eliminate a lot of modern art, wouldn't it?" Tyndall would suggest helpfully.

"What? How can you be so blind? Why do you misunderstand him? The words 'at sight' really mean 'when seen', or 'when perceived', which would take in a lot of modern art, Tyndall." Then the tiredness would go from his eyes, he would lean across the table, "Look here, you say you're fond of painting, Tyndall. I'd like to hear what you say about form. Just your own perception . . ." And then the eager, irritating, exasperating discussion would begin and last sometimes until two o'clock, with Tyndall always feeling fresh and young and content.

"It's an odd thing," Tyndall said, walking Adams back to Elmsley Place. "I met you for the first time in the Hart House barber shop, didn't I?"

"What's odd about that, Tyndall?"

"Well, some years ago a student told me he only came to Hart House when he wanted to get a haircut. The barber shop, do you see, Adams? Well, it annoyed me. Yet, it was a little landmark in my adventures around here."

"So? I don't get it."

"Well, that Hart House barber shop," Tyndall said, chuckling to himself, "evidently had possibilities I didn't suspect at the time. I've come a long way. Well, good night. I'll be around again."

CHAPTER THIRTEEN

HEN the second Great War broke out the whole life of the University was dislocated. Tyndall was then in his forty-fourth year. He had got a little plumper, his hair line had thinned, and he had streaks of iron gray at his temples. It was not necessary for Tyndall to go to war; but he was single, he saw young students who were just beginning their university lives giving up their dreams, and he had, too, a sentimental attachment to England and France. The army could use him as an educational officer, he said. Those who tried to discourage him found him adamant. His whole training, he said, had prepared him for the kind of work the army would expect of him. Besides, he added, with his dry little smile, he rather looked forward to seeing England again on a nice long leave of absence.

He had arranged to leave Hart House for the army after the Christmas holiday. One night in December in the last week of the term he had gone to a concert in Eaton Auditorium. When he came out it was snowing, the streets were an inch deep in snow. Soft heavy wet flakes drifted aimlessly across the street light. The air was soft and mild and there was no wind. The whiteness of the ground and the falling snow made him feel isolated, meditative and unusually restless, and although he did not have his rubbers on, he began to walk west on College Street toward the University.

How it happened he did not know—it might have been the fact that he was walking through a curtain of snow toward the university buildings—but soon he seemed to be walking back through his own life. Each little landmark became a poignant reminder of the past. At the Connaught Laboratories he stopped for a moment and smiled and remembered the lunch he had had in there with bright and well-informed people. The snow trickled down his neck and melted on his upturned face; his feet were getting wet. At last he walked on. At the corner of University and College, in the Conservatory of Music, lights were still in the windows, and someone was playing a fiddle. It seemed to be just the right kind of music for that mild winter night. He hadn't gone into the Conservatory often enough. He hadn't really got to know Sir Ernest MacMillan. It was a pity, because he was really fond of music. After all, he played the flute pretty well.

As he turned up the crescent the headlights of the car coming down seemed to be circling around his own life because he was following in the familiar paths of all his old doubts about Toronto. Suddenly he couldn't bear to make the little turn at the place where the path leads down the steps into the valley, back of the library; he couldn't bear to get a sudden glimpse of the campus and the dark snow-shadowed University College and Hart House, his home. In the snow there would be no paths made by students, no lights in the College windows; it would look like a deserted place, emptied of all the life he had lived there,

162

all gone as he, himself, was going. The things he had done, the songs he sang, the fierce arguments, the vast doubts, and the unending pursuit of a solution for his little problem, all were part of a life that had been smoothed away by the blanket of untrodden whiteness. In the morning new paths would be trampled, the doors would all open; but after this night, for a long time at least, the new paths would not be used by him.

Then he went round the bend and past the bushes, and as an approaching car headlight shone on him he stood with his hands deep in his pockets, a little crown of snow on his hat, staring across the campus at Convocation Hall. It was hard to see the outline in the snow. The sky seemed to close down over all the buildings. The weird hum of a thousand voices was in his head, his own voice always among them. The shroud of snow, getting thicker, closed in on him, and against the heavy sky he could hardly see the dark mound which was Knox College. Many of the Knox men had become friendly with him and yet it was still a fact that he had not been in Knox College. Smiling he assured himself that one of the first things he would do when he returned would be to spend an hour or two in Knox; then suddenly he felt an ache in his heart.

It came from the recollection of his unending, quiet pursuit of a pattern for the fields of knowledge represented by those buildings. Some years ago—it seemed like yesterday—he had stood in the park feeling like a painter working on the little part of a great design he might never see, yet believing that the design was there. But not to try to see it any more! Why did it sadden him? It wouldn't bother him again. Its elusiveness now wouldn't matter. Then why this feeling of discontent and loneliness when he could stop looking for a thing he couldn't find? Perhaps he had loved looking for it. He had fallen in love with the elusiveness of the pattern which he had sought, its mystery had enchanted

163

him and driven him on as a man follows in his dreams a lovely woman who is an enigma, loving her because she is fugitive and always an enigma.

It would change around there now, of course. All would change, for all the intellectual resources of the University would be harnessed as much as possible to the war effort. Those men in the Physics Department, whose time he had wasted so often, would work for the Admiralty, the air force, the army. All the young doctors would be drafted into the Services. The engineers would not be troubled for some time by little jibes about culture from the Arts men. Those splendid technicians who were the pride of the University would become key men. In the research labs incredible explosives of devastating power would be devised by the quiet men of the Chemistry Department. The lights in the labs would burn all night, but the lights in the windows of the Arts colleges . . . well, a lot of them would go out. The Arts man would be of less consequence than he had ever been. Who wants to listen to a lover of the humanities in war time? He could wither up, or hide or patiently be brushed aside. He would become even less than he was . . .

"Why, yes," thought Tyndall, forgetting how slowly he was walking and how wet his feet were. "A time like this really makes it clear."

But as he sloshed on through the snow he began to wonder why he had been looking around at all those familiar places as if he were convinced in his heart that he would never see them again. Why, it was absurd! When the war was over he would return. Everybody counted on coming back. And since he was only going to be an education officer, what did he imagine could happen to him? The crossing to England. Yes, ships were being sunk every day in the North Atlantic; but even when a ship was torpedoed most of the survivors were picked up. And if bombs were falling in England, well, for that matter, people were being hit by automobiles every day on the streets of Toronto. It could happen to anybody. No one knew when his number was up. With a shrug he brushed away such thoughts.

If he felt a little melancholy, he told himself, it was only because of the white silence of the night and his being alone here, with the snow falling on the campus and shrouding the trees in Queen's Park, each college building, the entire city. He was feeling as that lawyer must have felt years ago—the one he had encountered while crossing the playing-field at the Varsity Stadium after the game—what was his name? He had said, 'Ghosts, Tyndall. Ghosts." Yes, he knew how the lawyer must have felt, only now, he, Tyndall, saw himself reliving a little scene in the most unexpected place. He did not see himself with important people; the voices he seemed to hear were neither authoritative nor eloquent. He saw himself going into the dressing-room at the Stadium after a game with Queen's which had ended in a bitter, unexpected defeat. He had hardly ever gone into a dressing-room, but it was the last game of the season and he had wanted to congratulate the coach and some players he knew.

The room was filled with the strong smell of liniment and sweat and soaked football gear. Standing at the door he hesitated. Usually, a dressing-room after a game, especially if there has been a victory, is full of noisy chatter and kidding and beefing: all the players are still keyed up, they have to get rid of the tension in some kind of clowning and horseplay. But that day there was no chatter and no exuberant gestures, just an all-pervading air of grim despondency. Some players sat on the benches, with their arms hanging loosely between their knees, their faces smeared with sweat and mud. Some were slowly dragging off their soiled sweaters. One was lying on the rubbing table, half naked, his chest rising and falling as he gasped for air. Steam seemed to be rising from all their bodies, and at that moment they were like massive, heavy-shouldered monsters, tired and beaten and herded into a gloomy, steaming cavern. But as he had entered, some of them had looked up, and in their red, tired and dirty faces he had caught a glimpse of something which he had never forgotten. It was a hard yet quiet inner intensity: each face had its peculiar independent but democratic expression. Even in that hour of dejected exhaustion their faces showed the splendid virtue they weren't even aware of. He had wanted very much to have them believe that he was truly one of them.

As he recalled this scene, wondering why it should have flashed into his mind just now, he realized that he was deeply moved. Suddenly he understood clearly his premonition that he would not return to Hart House and Varsity. A man sees all such little things through his heart, dwells on the things that truly move him, knows the years to remember, only at the time of a final parting.

In the morning he had a very bad cold; he had to go to bed and it bothered him because at the end of the week, the last week of the term, he was to give his Hart House Christmas dinner to those students who were far from home. He had invited thirty or so, only about ten from Ontario, and the rest from places as far away as India, the Yukon, Chile and South Africa. He also invited his friend, the history professor who had thought of himself as a coral ant, and that engineer whom he had quarrelled with.

The doctor insisted that Tyndall had influenza and ought to stay in bed over the week-end or he would be in danger of pneumonia. He did stay in bed for two days, but on the third day, the day of his dinner, he had faith in his strong constitution and got up. All that bothered him was a cold in the head that made his voice thick, and uncontrollable fits of sneezing, which might easily spoil this Christmas party which had become extraordinarily important to him.

This party was to be his farewell gesture to the students. It was important to him for that reason.

But he was there at his Christmas dinner smiling and talking through his nose and using his handkerchief a lot. The long table was arranged at the north end of the great hall, not too far away from the hearth. On the panels over the hearth were the arms of seventy-four universities of the Allied Nations of the first Great War, and now, of course, there was another war and a new set of allied nations; but the fire glowed in the hearth and the shadows in the great vaulted beamed ceiling were broken by shifting firelight. As he carved the turkey Tyndall looked round at the faces of those thirty who were strangers in the city. Among them were engineers, Arts men, medical men. Tyndall knew how to preside at these dinners with a quiet, happy, friendly dignity that helped his guests to relax and feel at ease with each other. A Christmas dinner table is not a place for men who are strangers. The Hindu, the Chilean, the man from South Africa and the man from the Yukon soon began to feel that they were in their own home because they were in that Great Hall with Tyndall.

"Gentlemen," Tyndall said, standing up when they were all stuffed and ready to sit back and feel warm and drowsy, "It isn't my custom to make a little speech at these dinners. Speeches are a bore after a pleasant dinner. But I'll be going away soon and there is something I want to say because many of you are strangers in the city as I was once a stranger. Do you mind if I go on?"

"Hear, hear," they cried.

"Go on, Tyndall," said the engineer. They all seemed to know that Tyndall wanted to say something important to them. He had started to cough, and he apologized while he blew his nose. "I have a confession to make," he said with a smile, and so everyone else smiled too. They couldn't imagine Tyndall making a confession that would trouble anyone. "I'm ashamed to reveal this, but I'll feel better if I do. After I had been here about a year," he went on gravely, "I realized I had a rather low opinion of this University. I hid my real feelings. In a sense, I suppose, I was a first-class hypocrite."

"Nonsense," someone muttered.

"I'm telling the truth," he insisted. "I had every intention of leaving here. I—well, I was simply disappointed. Then why did I stay on? I got interested, that's all. I started off on a wild-goose chase, and I think I got to love the chase, for the end of the chase was always over the hills, but the hills were always beyond the horizon." His head was on one side, the light from the fireplace just touched his cheeks and he seemed to be off by himself, thinking, and wanting to say freshly the truth as it came quickly in his thoughts. The thirty students grew shy and the two professors looked embarrassed. They knew he was speaking out of his heart.

"I thought the people around here were cautious and withdrawing," he said. "They seemed to be like people who were always hiding something. I know now they are good, friendly, independent, unpretentious people. I belong with them wherever I go. But I looked for a way of life around here. I wondered if the fields of knowledge organized here were expressed in a pattern that got into the life of a man. I was going round trying to catch a tone, an atmosphere, something belonging to the whole community. I know that the Arts men are supposed to give a university its tone, but I never could make up my mind what was lacking. The Arts men are so peculiarly self-effacing; you know, one of them told me once that he didn't mind being anonymous," he said, smiling at the historian, who blinked, and then smiled cheerfully. "And I think he told the truth about most of the Arts men. They don't mind being anonymous. But it's pretty hard to identify anybody who is anonymous, isn't it?"

"Go on, Tyndall," the historian said.

"Go ahead," said the engineer.

"Well, one day when I was standing down near the Parliament Buildings a young medical student in a trench coat came along. It was raining that day. I had known him when he was in the pass course. In the summer he had worked on the lake boats and somewhere or other had picked up a copy of Sir William Osler's lectures to medical students. He used to read Osler on the boats. Well, his imagination was excited and he came rushing back to college all aglow to become a doctor. It's odd, you know, but the day I saw that lad walking in the rain I knew that his story had something to do with that thing I was looking for, that missing link, the tone, the break in the pattern. I was right, too. It was there under my eyes—in that student, but I couldn't see it plainly till the other night when I was walking in the snow and got this cold," he said, taking out his handkerchief and blowing his nose again.

"What was it?" the engineer asked.

"I shouldn't have missed it, it was so plain," Tyndall went on. "Osler was not anonymous. That's it. In his writing and in his point of view, firing the soul of that boy, he was not anonymous. I think it came through for the boy that he was a remarkable and exalting personality. Anyway, he created a personal passion in that boy. It was all intensely personal and human. A great doctor communicating as a great civilized person. Of course the clue I had been missing was right there," he said, growing a little embarrassed because the history professor leaned closer to him. "What I had been missing around here was all emphasis on the person, the greatness of the person. Anonymous men become impersonal men. Oh, I know the impersonal touch is in the air now. It comes out of the lab, and the technicians have to use it, and it seems to be accepted as the mark of scholarship, but sooner or later they have to come out of the labs and live with people in a personal relationship. Well, I don't like to see the Arts men accepting their fate humbly just because they are crowded to the wall in our technological civilization. I can't see how the anonymous impersonal man can give a tone to anything. I don't see how he can teach men how to live. Well, I learned something about life from every line of poetry I committed to memory, and from the philosophers too. Oh, I won't go on with it, but if the Arts man, too, becomes anonymous and impersonal I think you might as well close up his colleges."

There was an awkward silence, so he fumbled again for his handkerchief, blew his nose, cleared his throat, and smiled in embarrassment. "I keep coming back to that medical student walking in the rain," he went on. "He's been in my mind a long time, you see. The greatness of the person, eh? Well, some of you will say it has nothing to do with education—maybe not. But I've read some of those histories of what they call 'idiot savants', and you have too, I'm sure. Those strange creatures who have been confined to asylums, though they have astounding genius in mathematics, or in feats of memory, or in music or engineering. Yet they are idiots! They can't be allowed to remain at large. They don't know how to live with people. As persons they are unbalanced. They have no personal wisdom. Specialist wisdom—oh, true enough! . . . Well, I believe now that the medical student, stirred by the Osler lectures, grasped in his imagination the relationship between wisdom about one's work and wisdom in living and wanted the two things to become one in his own person. But I'll stop here: I can't prove it, can I?"

170

Then the historian asked suddenly, "What about that design, Tyndall? Seeing the thing as a whole."

"Well, I tried to find it," Tyndall said with a sigh, "but like Peer Gynt I'm home with you now and I bring back no glowing pattern I can describe or say I saw, but only a very humble truth. I'm still convinced that the separate colleges, the different schools, are there making some kind of a pattern, but no one may ever see it. It's there like a giant crystal—if you are restless and can dream and look far ahead, you yourselves may be wiser than I have been about it. I'll go on thinking the different colleges and the different kinds of learning are all like facets of the one crystal. I could only see one facet at a time, but I think each facet is an aspect of the truth, and those separate facets can glisten and shine and perhaps, if you are poets or philosophers, give you a glimpse of the whole truth that I couldn't get."

A little hush had come over his listeners because he had a happy dreamy expression on his face. He was still talking quietly, easily, slowly. "I really shared my intellectual adventure in Toronto with all of you. We were all on our separate quests, scholars, research workers, practical men—seeking an answer to an intellectual riddle, or seeking a form for our lives. I read somewhere that in fifteenth-century Spain one saint would meet another saint on the highway and ask, 'Which way are you following?' for they knew there were many ways. And there are many ways here too. Well, it was quite a long speech, gentlemen, but I'm through for the evening. I'm leaving you now. I promised my doctor I'd go back to bed right after dinner and nurse this cold. There's a little gift for each one of you. My two friends here will look after you. So, gentlemen, good night and a happy New Year."

As he turned away from the table they all stood up and one of the students called, "Give him a cheer," but he looked dreadfully embarrassed. "Please don't," he pleaded. "It's not in the Christmas spirit, you know," so they crowded around him shaking his hand and wishing him luck. The engineer clasped his hand warmly. The historian, walking along the hall with him, said, "You don't mind the company of an anonymous friend?"

"I do hope you don't mind what I said."

"You shouldn't have applied it just to the Arts men, but the whole country, Tyndall," he said laughing. "Let's hear from you some time, eh."

"Of course," Tyndall said. "Good night."

He went up to his own rooms, sat down with his arms folded, sat there for a long time, not moving; then he looked up suddenly, remembered that he had a cold and went to bed.